An Introduction to
THE CALCULUS
of
FINITE DIFFERENCES

C. H. RICHARDSON

Late Professor of Mathematics
Bucknell University

D. VAN NOSTRAND COMPANY, INC.

PRINCETON, NEW JERSEY

TORONTO LONDON

NEW YORK

D. VAN NOSTRAND COMPANY, INC.
120 Alexander St., Princeton, New Jersey (*Principal office*)
24 West 40 Street, New York 18, New York

D. VAN NOSTRAND COMPANY, LTD.
358, Kensington High Street, London, W.14, England

D. VAN NOSTRAND COMPANY (Canada), LTD.
25 Hollinger Road, Toronto 16, Canada

Library of Congress Catalogue Card No. 54–5779

First Published February 1954
Reprinted January 1958, February 1960,
August 1963, May 1966

PREFACE

A number of years ago, to meet the demands of our students in actuarial and statistical theory, we began offering a semester course in the essentials of the finite calculus. Within recent years the course has proved attractive also to our students in electrical engineering and physics. This "Introduction" presents the content of our course which regularly appears on our program as an elective for juniors and seniors.

Since no prerequisite other than an elementary course in infinitesimal calculus is assumed, we make no pretense at imposing undue rigor. The emphasis is on method, and numerous exercises are provided to fix the principles.

The real reason for the appearance of the book is simply this: no modern elementary text is available. Excellent books suitable for the advanced student are at hand. The books [1] by Fort, Milne-Thompson, and Jordan are too severe in their background requirements for the American student at the junior level. The books by Milne-Thompson and Jordan are veritable encyclopedias but not at all suited to our needs. Of course, Nörlund's work [1] is unsurpassed, but it too is a treatise and not suitable as an introductory text. Further, unfortunately for us in America, it is written in German and no translation into English has yet appeared.

The subject matter of the finite calculus goes back more than two hundred years to Daniel and Jakob Bernoulli, Leonhard Euler, Jacobo Stirling, and others. The literature concerning it is colossal as can be observed by looking at the bibliography in Nörlund's great work. All we have hoped to do is to make available the minimum essentials for a semester course. When the reader, in addition to this text, has completed courses in advanced calculus, differential equations, and complex variable, he can then hopefully venture into the books we have mentioned.

I owe a debt of gratitude to my former students who have served as guinea pigs over the years as we have developed this course. They have

[1] See page 129.

iii

been most helpful with their sympathetic criticisms. I am also greatly indebted to Professor L. L. Garner of the University of North Carolina and to Doctor Ernest E. Blanche, Lecturer in Mathematics at The American University, Washington, D. C. Both of these gentlemen have used this book in mimeographed form in their classes for several years. Professor Garner has also assisted with the proofreading. They have been especially helpful in searching out errors. For any errors that remain I alone am responsible. For the notification of such errors, I shall be deeply appreciative.

C. H. RICHARDSON

Bucknell University,
Lewisburg, Pa.
December 30, 1953.

CONTENTS

Chapter I

INTRODUCTION

1. Definitions and Notation

The calculus of finite differences, in its broad meaning, deals with the changes that take place in the values of a function, the dependent variable, due to changes in the independent variable. Thus, if x is increased by an amount Δx, the function x^2 increases to $(x + \Delta x)^2$, and there is an increment of $(x + \Delta x)^2 - x^2 = 2x\Delta x + \overline{\Delta x}^2$ in the given function.

Functions of x are usually denoted by $f(x)$, $F(x)$, $\varphi(x)$, or by U, V, etc. In the calculus of finite differences, these modes of representation, in some measure, seem to be blended in that the dependent function of x is usually represented by U_x, the suffix taking the place of the symbol that is usually enclosed in parentheses. For example, if $U_x = x^2$, then $U_{x+\Delta x} = (x + \Delta x)^2$ and $U_{x+\Delta x} - U_x = 2x\Delta x + \overline{\Delta x}^2$.

The increment

$$U_{x+\Delta x} - U_x$$

which is the difference in the function U_x corresponding to an increment of Δx in x, is called the *first difference* of U_x, and is represented by

$$\underset{\Delta x}{\Delta} U_x = U_{x+\Delta x} - U_x$$

In the finite calculus generally Δx is constant. Denoting this constant by h, we have for the first difference of U_x

$$\underset{h}{\Delta} U_x = U_{x+h} - U_x \tag{1}$$

In our treatment the difference of the independent variable is constant. Consequently, the calculus of differences is a study of the relations that exist between the values assumed by the function whenever the independent variable takes on a series of values in arithmetic progression.

1

The result of performing the operation denoted by the operator Δ_h is still a function of x on which the operation may be repeated. We then obtain the *second difference*

$$\Delta_h(\Delta_h U_x) = (U_{x+2h} - U_{x+h}) - (U_{x+h} - U_x)$$

Denoting the second difference by $\Delta_h^2 U_x$, we have

$$\Delta_h^2 U_x = U_{x+2h} - 2U_{x+h} + U_x$$

Proceeding in this way we can form the third, fourth, $\cdots$, nth differences

$$\Delta_h^3 U_x, \; \Delta_h^4 U_x, \; \cdots, \; \Delta_h^n U_x$$

by means of the relation

$$\Delta_h^s U_x = \Delta_h(\Delta_h^{s-1} U_x)$$

Although h may be any constant value, the value usually given to it is unity. There are two reasons for this.

First, the calculus of finite differences has for an important topic of application the summation of series. Explicitly or implicitly, each term of a series is a function of the integer which fixes its position in the series, and thus the independent variable assumes only integral values which differ by unity. For example, the sequence

$$1^2, 2^2, 3^2, \cdots$$

has for its general or xth term x^2. It is an explicit function of x, but the values of x are the natural numbers and $h = 1$.

Second, when the general term of a series is a function of t, whose successive differences are constant but not equal to unity, we may replace the independent variable by another, x, whose common difference is unity. Let U_t be the function of t in which $\Delta t = h$; then, assuming the substitution $t = hx$, we have

$$\Delta t = \Delta(hx) = h(x + \Delta x) - hx = h\Delta x$$

Since $\Delta t = h$, we have $h = h\Delta x$ or $\Delta x = 1$.

Thus, it is sufficient to establish our laws on the assumption that the interval of differencing in the independent variable is unity. When this assumption is made, we shall adopt Δ instead of $\underset{1}{\Delta}$ as our symbol of operation, and thus our defining equation becomes

$$\Delta U_x = U_{x+1} - U_x \tag{2}$$

To illustrate:

$$\Delta x^2 = (x+1)^2 - x^2 = 2x + 1$$

$$\Delta \log x = \log (x+1) - \log x = \log \left(\frac{x+1}{x}\right) = \log \left(1 + \frac{1}{x}\right)$$

$$\Delta \sin x = \sin (x+1) - \sin x = 2 \sin \tfrac{1}{2} \cos (x + \tfrac{1}{2})$$

$$\Delta 2^x = 2^{x+1} - 2^x = 2^x (2 - 1) = 2^x$$

By means of (2) it easily follows that

$$\Delta(U_x \pm V_x) = \Delta U_x \pm \Delta V_x \tag{3}$$

Exercises

1. Find the first differences of the following:

(a) $3x^4$.

(b) $\cos x$.

(c) $\tan x$.

(d) a^x.

(e) $x(x-1)(x-2)(x-3)$.

(f) $x(x+1)(x+2)(x+3)$.

(g) $\sin^{-1} x$.

(h) $\log \sin x$.

(i) $x!$.

(j) x^n.

(k) $_xC_r = \binom{x}{r} = \dfrac{x(x-1)(x-2) \cdots (x-r+1)}{r!}$.

2. Show that

(a) $\Delta^3 U_x = U_{x+3} - 3U_{x+2} + 3U_{x+1} - U_x$.

(b) $\Delta^4 U_x = U_{x+4} - 4U_{x+3} + 6U_{x+2} - 4U_{x+1} + U_x$.

3. What function of x satisfies the equation $\Delta U_x = U_x$?

4. Find $\Delta^n U_x$ when U_x is

(a) a^x.

(b) e^{a+bx}.

5. Find ΔU_x if U_x is:

(a) $x(x-1)3^x$.

(b) $[x(x+1)(x+2)]^{-1}$.

(c) $\cot 2^x$.

(d) $ax^2 + bx + c$.

(e) $ax^3 + bx^2 + cx + d$.

6. Show that $\Delta^n x^n = n!$.

7. Using the method of trial and error find U_x if ΔU_x is:

(a) x, (b) x^2, (c) a^x, (d) x^3, (e) e^{a+bx}.

8. Show that $\Delta \dfrac{1}{2^{x-1}} \cot \dfrac{\theta}{2^{x-1}} = \dfrac{1}{2^x} \tan \dfrac{\theta}{2^x}$.

9. Show that $\Delta \left(2^{x-1} \sin \dfrac{\theta}{2^{x-1}} \right)^2 = \left(2^x \sin^2 \dfrac{\theta}{2^x} \right)^2$.

10. Show that $\Delta \left(\dfrac{1}{2^{x-1}} \csc \dfrac{\theta}{2^{x-1}} \right)^2 = - \left(\dfrac{1}{2^x} \sec \dfrac{\theta}{2^x} \right)^2$.

11. Show that $\Delta \cot 2^x\theta = -\frac{1}{2}[\tan 2^x\theta + \cot 2^x\theta] = - \csc 2^{x+1}\theta$.

12. Show that $\Delta 2^{x-2} \sin \dfrac{\theta}{2^{x-1}} = 2^x \sin \dfrac{\theta}{2^x} \left(\sin \dfrac{\theta}{2^{x+1}} \right)^2$.

13. Show that $\Delta \arctan x = \arctan \dfrac{1}{1 + x + x^2}$.

14. Show that $\Delta 2^x \cot 2^x\theta = -2^x \tan 2^x\theta$.

15. Show that $\Delta \tan \dfrac{\theta}{2^{x-1}} = - \tan \dfrac{\theta}{2^x} \sec \dfrac{\theta}{2^{x-1}}$.

16. Show that $\Delta \dfrac{\sin (x - 1)\theta \cos^x \theta}{\sin \theta} = \cos^x \theta \cos x\theta$.

17. Show that $\Delta \dfrac{\sin x\theta}{\sin \theta \cos^{x-1} \theta} = \cos x\theta \sec^x \theta$.

18. Show that $\Delta \dfrac{c^x(ax + b)}{x} = \dfrac{c^x[Ax^2 + Bx + D]}{x(x + 1)}$ when $\begin{cases} A = a(c - 1) \\ B = (a + b)(c - 1) \\ D = -b \end{cases}$

19. Show that $\Delta \left[- \dfrac{1}{2^{x-1}} \log (2 \sin 2^x\theta) \right] = \dfrac{1}{2^x} \log \tan 2^x\theta$.

20. Show that $\Delta \dfrac{1}{2} \cos \dfrac{\theta}{2^{x-3}} = \sin \dfrac{\theta}{2^{x-1}} \sin \dfrac{3\theta}{2^{x-1}}$.

21. Prove by induction: $(\cos x + i \sin x)^n = \cos nx + i \sin nx$ [DeMoivre's Theorem].

22. Prove: $\Delta \sinh (a + bx) = 2 \sinh \dfrac{b}{2} \cosh \left(a + \dfrac{b}{2} + bx \right)$.

23. Prove: $\Delta \cosh (a + bx) = 2 \sinh \dfrac{b}{2} \sinh \left(a + \dfrac{b}{2} + bx \right)$.

2. TABLES OF DIFFERENCES

The successive differences of a tabulated function are easily found from a table by subtraction, and from such a table, known as a *table of differences*, many important relations may be noted. Thus, for the function x^3 we have

TABLE 1. DIFFERENCES OF x^3

x	x^3	Δx^3	$\Delta^2 x^3$	$\Delta^3 x^3$	$\Delta^4 x^3$
0	0				
		1			
1	1		6		
		7		6	
2	8		12		0
		19		6	
3	27		18		0
		37		6	
4	64		24		
		61			
5	125				

The values in the columns show the successive differences. The first set Δx^3 is obtained by subtracting each number of x^3 from its successor. The second set $\Delta^2 x^3$ is obtained by subtracting each value of Δx^3 from its successor. It will be noted that the third differences are constant and that the fourth and higher differences are zero.

More generally, let U_x denote a function of x which has the values

$$\cdots U_{-3}, U_{-2}, U_{-1}, U_0, U_1, U_2, U_3 \cdots$$

corresponding to equidistant values

$$\cdots -3, -2, -1, 0, 1, 2, 3, \cdots$$

of x. Table 2 shows the differences of all orders to and including $\Delta^5 U_x$.

TABLE 2. DIAGONAL DIFFERENCE TABLE

x	U_x	ΔU_x	$\Delta^2 U_x$	$\Delta^3 U_x$	$\Delta^4 U_x$	$\Delta^5 U_x$
-3	U_{-3}					
		ΔU_{-3}				
-2	U_{-2}		$\Delta^2 U_{-3}$			
		ΔU_{-2}		$\Delta^3 U_{-3}$		
-1	U_{-1}		$\Delta^2 U_{-2}$		$\Delta^4 U_{-3}$	
		ΔU_{-1}		$\Delta^3 U_{-2}$		$\Delta^5 U_{-3}$
0	U_0		$\Delta^2 U_{-1}$		$\Delta^4 U_{-2}$	
		ΔU_0		$\Delta^3 U_{-1}$		$\Delta^5 U_{-2}$
1	U_1		$\Delta^2 U_0$		$\Delta^4 U_{-1}$	
		ΔU_1		$\Delta^3 U_0$		
2	U_2		$\Delta^2 U_1$			
		ΔU_2				
3	U_3					

Table 2 is called a *diagonal difference table*. The majority of difference tables are of this kind, but for many purposes a more compact table—a *horizontal difference table*—shown in Table 3, is preferable.

TABLE 3. HORIZONTAL DIFFERENCE TABLE

x	U_x	ΔU_x	$\Delta^2 U_x$	$\Delta^3 U_x$	$\Delta^4 U_x$	$\Delta^5 U_x$	$\Delta^6 U_x$
-3	U_{-3}	ΔU_{-3}	$\Delta^2 U_{-3}$	$\Delta^3 U_{-3}$	$\Delta^4 U_{-3}$	$\Delta^5 U_{-3}$	$\Delta^6 U_{-3}$
-2	U_{-2}	ΔU_{-2}	$\Delta^2 U_{-2}$	$\Delta^3 U_{-2}$	$\Delta^4 U_{-2}$	$\Delta^5 U_{-2}$	
-1	U_{-1}	ΔU_{-1}	$\Delta^2 U_{-1}$	$\Delta^3 U_{-1}$	$\Delta^4 U_{-1}$		
0	U_0	ΔU_0	$\Delta^2 U_0$	$\Delta^3 U_0$			
1	U_1	ΔU_1	$\Delta^2 U_1$				
2	U_2	ΔU_2					
3	U_3						

The differences in the downward diagonal of Table 2 setting out from a function and having the same subscript as the function are called the *leading differences* of the value of the function. Thus, ΔU_0, $\Delta^2 U_0$, $\Delta^3 U_0$, and so on are called the leading differences of U_0.

In the horizontal difference table the value of a function and its leading differences are in the same row.

The construction of either the diagonal difference table or the horizontal difference table requires that we keep in mind, as previously defined, that

$$\Delta U_x = U_{x+1} - U_x$$

or, more generally,

$$\Delta^{k+1} U_x = \Delta^k U_{x+1} - \Delta^k U_x$$

Although we have expressed the terms of the difference table by the use of Δ symbols, it is quite easy to obtain any difference in terms of the values of U_x. For example,

$$\Delta U_0 = U_1 - U_0$$

$$\Delta U_1 = U_2 - U_1$$

$$\Delta U_2 = U_3 - U_2$$

$$\cdot \quad \cdot \quad \cdot \quad \cdot \quad \cdot \quad \cdot \quad \cdot \quad \cdot$$

$$\Delta U_n = U_{n+1} - U_n$$

Similarly,

$$\Delta^2 U_0 = \Delta U_1 - \Delta U_0 = U_2 - 2U_1 + U_0$$

$$\Delta^2 U_1 = \Delta U_2 - \Delta U_1 = U_3 - 2U_2 + U_1$$

$$\Delta^2 U_2 = \Delta U_3 - \Delta U_2 = U_4 - 2U_3 + U_2$$

and so on.

In like manner, the third differences are

$$\Delta^3 U_0 = \Delta^2 U_1 - \Delta^2 U_0 = U_3 - 3U_2 + 3U_1 - U_0$$
$$\Delta^3 U_1 = \Delta^2 U_2 - \Delta^2 U_1 = U_4 - 3U_3 + 3U_2 - U_1$$

and so on.

These relationships are easily derived by building up a table of differences. Thus, Table 4 exhibits these relationships in a compact form.

TABLE 4. DIFFERENCES IN TERMS OF VALUES OF U_x

x	U_x	ΔU_x	$\Delta^2 U_x$	$\Delta^3 U_x$
0	U_0	$U_1 - U_0$	$U_2 - 2U_1 + U_0$	$U_3 - 3U_2 + 3U_1 - U_0$
1	U_1	$U_2 - U_1$	$U_3 - 2U_2 + U_1$	$U_4 - 3U_3 + 3U_2 - U_1$
2	U_2	$U_3 - U_2$	$U_4 - 2U_3 + U_2$	$U_5 - 3U_4 + 3U_3 - U_2$
3	U_3	$U_4 - U_3$	$U_5 - 2U_4 + U_3$	
4	U_4	$U_5 - U_4$		
5	U_5			

Exercises

1. By constructing difference tables find:
   (a) The sixth term of the sequence 8, 12, 19, 29, 42, $\cdots$.
   (b) The seventh and eighth terms of the sequence 0, 0, 2, 6, 12, 20, $\cdots$.
   (c) The first term of the sequence whose second and subsequent terms are 8, 3, 0, -1, 0, $\cdots$.
   (d) The tenth term of the sequence 3, 14, 39, 84, 155, 258.
2. Prove that $U_3 = U_2 + \Delta U_1 + \Delta^2 U_0 + \Delta^3 U_0$.
3. Find U_6 given $U_0 = -3$, $U_1 = 6$, $U_2 = 8$, $U_3 = 12$, the third differences being constant.
4. Find Δab^{cx} and $\Delta^2 ab^{cx}$.
5. Find $\Delta^n U_x$ where U_x is (1) ax^n, (2) $x(x-1)(x-2) \cdots (x-n+1)$.
6. If $U_x = e^{ax}$, show that U_0 and its leading differences form a geometric progression.

3. DIFFERENCE FORMULAS

In this section we shall develop certain theorems that are useful in the difference calculus.

Theorem 1. If c is a constant, $\Delta c = 0$.

Proof. $\Delta c = c - c = 0$.

Further, if C_x is a periodic function of period unity, that is, if $C_{x+1} = C_x$, then $\Delta C_x = 0$.

Theorem 2. If U_x, V_x, and W_x are functions of x,

$$\Delta^n(U_x + V_x - W_x) = \Delta^n U_x + \Delta^n V_x - \Delta^n W_x$$

Proof.

$$\Delta(U_x + V_x - W_x) = U_{x+1} + V_{x+1} - W_{x+1} - U_x - V_x + W_x$$

$$= (U_{x+1} - U_x) + (V_{x+1} - V_x) - (W_{x+1} - W_x)$$

$$= \Delta U_x + \Delta V_x - \Delta W_x$$

Repeating this process,

$$\Delta[\Delta(U_x + V_x - W_x)] = \Delta[\Delta U_x + \Delta V_x - \Delta W_x]$$

$$= \Delta^2 U_x + \Delta^2 V_x - \Delta^2 W_x$$

That is,

$$\Delta^2(U_x + V_x - W_x) = \Delta^2 U_x + \Delta^2 V_x - \Delta^2 W_x$$

By induction the theorem follows immediately.

Theorem 3. If c is a constant, and U_x a function of x,

$$\Delta^n c U_x = c \Delta^n U_x$$

Proof.

$$\Delta c U_x = c U_{x+1} - c U_x = c(U_{x+1} - U_x) = c \Delta U_x$$

$$\Delta^2 c U_x = \Delta(\Delta c U_x) = \Delta[c(\Delta U_x)] = c \Delta(\Delta U_x) = c \Delta^2 U_x$$

By induction the theorem follows.

If C_x is a periodic function of period unity, $\Delta C_x U_x = C_x \Delta U_x$.

Theorem 4. $\Delta^n x^n = n!$ when n is a positive integer.

Proof.

$$\Delta x^n = (x + 1)^n - x^n$$

$$= n x^{n-1} + \text{terms of lower degree than } (n - 1)$$

Each repetition of the process of differencing reduces the degree by unity and also adds one factor to the succession $n(n - 1)(n - 2) \cdots$. Repeating the process n times we have

$$\Delta^n x^n = n!$$

as stated in the theorem.

Corollary 1. $\Delta^n a x^n = a(n!)$.

Corollary 2. $\Delta^{n+1} x^n = 0$.

Corollary 3. If U_x is a polynomial in x of degree n:

$$U_x = A_0 x^n + A_1 x^{n-1} + \cdots + A_n$$

then
$$\Delta^n U_x = A_0(n!)$$

Definition. The continued products

$$U_x U_{x+1} U_{x+2} \cdots U_{x+n-1}$$

$$U_x U_{x-1} U_{x-2} \cdots U_{x-n+1}$$

are called *factorial expressions.* The subscripts in the progressions may increase or decrease by a constant quantity.

Applying the operator Δ to the first of the above expressions and simplifying, we have

$$\Delta U_x U_{x+1} \cdots U_{x+n-1} = (U_{x+n} - U_x)(U_{x+1} U_{x+2} \cdots U_{x+n-1})$$

Our most useful functions in finite differences are those in which $(U_{x+n} - U_x)$ is constant. For example, if $U_x = a + bx$, $(U_{x+n} - U_x) = nb$. Two important factorial forms are defined by the equations:

$$(a + bx)^{|n|} = (a + bx)(a + \overline{bx + 1}) \cdots (a + \overline{bx + n - 1}),$$
$$(a + bx)^{|0|} = 1$$

$$(a + bx)^{(n)} = (a + bx)(a + \overline{bx - 1}) \cdots (a + \overline{bx - n + 1}),$$
$$(a + bx)^{(0)} = 1$$

In these equations, $(a + bx)$ is the *base* and n is the *index*. The index n indicates the number of factors in the product.

For the special case $a = 0$ and $b = 1$ we have

$$x^{|n|} = x(x + 1)(x + 2) \cdots (x + n - 1)$$
$$x^{(n)} = x(x - 1)(x - 2) \cdots (x - n + 1)$$

Theorem 5. $\Delta(a + bx)^{(n)} = bn(a + bx)^{(n-1)}.$

Proof.

$$\Delta(a + bx)^{(n)} = (a + \overline{bx + 1})(a + bx) \cdots (a + \overline{bx - n + 2})$$
$$- (a + bx)(a + \overline{bx - 1}) \cdots (a + \overline{bx - n + 1})$$
$$= (a + bx)(a + \overline{bx - 1}) \cdots (a + \overline{bx - n + 2})$$
$$[(a + \overline{bx + 1}) - (a + \overline{bx - n + 1})]$$
$$= bn(a + bx)^{(n-1)}$$

Corollary 1. $\Delta x^{(n)} = n x^{(n-1)}.$
Corollary 2. $\Delta^n x^{(n)} = n!.$
We shall leave it as an exercise for the student to prove:

Theorem 6. $\Delta \dfrac{1}{(a + bx)^{|n|}} = \dfrac{-bn}{(a + bx)^{|n+1|}}.$

Corollary 1. $\Delta \dfrac{1}{x^{|n|}} = \dfrac{-n}{x^{|n+1|}}.$

The reader will note the analogy between Theorems 5 and 6 with their corollaries and similar theorems in the infinitesimal calculus. Thus

Difference Calculus	*Infinitesimal Calculus*
$\Delta(a + bx)^{(n)} = bn(a + bx)^{(n-1)}$	$D(a + bx)^n = bn(a + bx)^{n-1}$
$\Delta x^{(n)} = nx^{(n-1)}$	$D(x^n) = nx^{n-1}$
$\Delta^n x^{(n)} = n!$	$D^n(x^n) = n!$
$\Delta \dfrac{1}{(a + bx)^{|n|}} = \dfrac{-bn}{(a + bx)^{|n+1|}}$	$D\left(\dfrac{1}{(a + bx)^n}\right) = \dfrac{-bn}{(a + bx)^{n+1}}$

Due to the fact that $x^{(n)}$ plays in the calculus of finite differences a role similar to that played by x^n in the infinitesimal calculus, for many purposes in finite differences it is advisable to express a given polynomial in a series of factorials. A method of accomplishing this is contained in Newton's Theorem.

Theorem 7. (Newton's Theorem) If U_x is a polynomial of the nth degree in x, it may be written in the form [1]

$$U_x = U_0 + x^{(1)}\Delta U_0 + \frac{x^{(2)}}{2!}\Delta^2 U_0 + \frac{x^{(3)}}{3!}\Delta^3 U_0 + \cdots + \frac{x^{(n)}}{n!}\Delta^n U_0$$

Proof. Assume [2]

$$U_x = a_0 + a_1 x^{(1)} + a_2 x^{(2)} + a_3 x^{(3)} + \cdots + a_n x^{(n)}$$

Differencing U_x n times, we have

$$\Delta U_x = a_1 + 2a_2 x^{(1)} + 3a_3 x^{(2)} + \cdots + na_n x^{(n-1)}$$

$$\Delta^2 U_x = 2 \cdot 1 \cdot a_2 + 3 \cdot 2 \cdot a_3 x^{(1)} + \cdots + n(n-1)a_n x^{(n-2)}$$

$$\Delta^3 U_x = 3 \cdot 2 \cdot 1 \cdot a_3 + \cdots + n(n-1)(n-2)a_n x^{(n-3)}$$

$$\cdots \cdots \cdots \cdots \cdots \cdots$$

$$\Delta^n U_x = a_n(n!)$$

Since these differences and U_x are identities, they are true for all values of x, and consequently must hold for $x = 0$. Setting $x = 0$ in the given function and the differences, we have

---

[1] This formula is analogous to Maclaurin's expansion in the infinitesimal calculus.

[2] This is certainly a legitimate assumption since the right-hand member is a polynomial of degree n with $(n + 1)$ arbitrary constants.

$$a_0 = U_0, \quad a_1 = \Delta U_0, \quad a_2 = \frac{\Delta^2 U_0}{2!}, \quad \cdots, \quad a_n = \frac{\Delta^n U_0}{n!}$$

Substituting these values in the right-hand side of the expression for U_x, we have the theorem as stated.

We shall now consider some applications of Theorem 7.

Example 1. Find the ninth term U_8 of the sequence: $U_0 = 1$, $U_1 = 4$, $U_2 = 10$, $U_3 = 20$, $U_4 = 35$, $U_5 = 56$, etc., assuming U_x is a polynomial.

To determine the leading differences of U_0 we shall form a difference table.

x	U_x	ΔU_x	$\Delta^2 U_x$	$\Delta^3 U_x$	$\Delta^4 U_x$
0	1	3	3	1	0
1	4	6	4	1	0
2	10	10	5	1	
3	20	15	6		
4	35	21			
5	56				

From Theorem 7, we have

$$U_8 = U_0 + 8\Delta U_0 + \frac{8 \cdot 7}{2!} \Delta^2 U_0 + \frac{8 \cdot 7 \cdot 6}{3!} \Delta^3 U_0$$

and from the table

$$U_0 = 1, \quad \Delta U_0 = 3, \quad \Delta^2 U_0 = 3, \quad \Delta^3 U_0 = 1, \quad \Delta^4 U_0 = 0$$

We thus find

$$U_8 = 1 + 8 \cdot 3 + 28 \cdot 3 + 56 \cdot 1 = 165$$

Example 2. Find the general term U_x for the data of Ex. 1.

$$U_x = U_0 + x^{(1)} \Delta U_0 + \frac{x^{(2)}}{2!} \Delta^2 U_0 + \frac{x^{(3)}}{3!} \Delta^3 U_0$$

$$= 1 + x^{(1)} \cdot 3 + \frac{x(x-1)}{2} \cdot 3 + \frac{x(x-1)(x-2)}{6} \cdot 1$$

$$= \tfrac{1}{6}[x^3 + 6x^2 + 11x + 6]$$

Example 3. Express $2x^3 - 3x^2 + 3x - 10$ in a series of factorials by two methods.

To solve this problem by Newton's Theorem we shall need U_0 and its leading differences. Hence we must build up a difference table for the given function $U_x = 2x^3 - 3x^2 + 3x - 10$. We note that U_0 and leading differences are $-10, 2, 6, 12$. Hence,

$$U_x = -10 + 2x^{(1)} + \frac{6x^{(2)}}{2!} + \frac{12x^{(3)}}{3!}$$

x	U_x	ΔU_x	$\Delta^2 U_x$	$\Delta^3 U_x$
0	-10	2	6	12
1	-8	8	18	
2	0	26		
3	26			

A second method, based upon the remainder theorem, gives the results more quickly. To review, the remainder theorem states: If a polynomial $f(x)$ is divided by $(x - a)$, the remainder is $f(a)$. We shall illustrate its use in this connection by applying it to the given problem, then we shall give a general discussion of the method.

Let

$$U_x = 2x^3 - 3x^2 + 3x - 10 \equiv Ax(x - 1)(x - 2) + Bx(x - 1) + Cx + D$$

If $x = 0$, $D = -10$, which, by the remainder theorem, is the value of the remainder when U_x is divided by x. By synthetic division this appears as

$$
\begin{array}{r|rrrr}
0 & 2 & -3 & +3 & -10 \\
  &   & +0 & +0 & -0 \\
\hline
  & 2 & -3 & +3 & -10 = D
\end{array}
$$

showing the quotient $2x^2 - 3x + 3$ and the remainder $-10 = U_0 = D$.

Our given identity now becomes

$$2x^3 - 3x^2 + 3x - 10 \equiv Ax(x - 1)(x - 2) + Bx(x - 1) + Cx - 10$$

which, upon simplification, reduces to

$$2x^2 - 3x + 3 \equiv A(x-1)(x-2) + B(x-1) + C$$

If, now $x = 1$ in the preceding equation, $C = 2$, which, by the remainder theorem, is the value of the remainder when $2x^2 - 3x + 3$ is divided by $(x-1)$. By synthetic division the work appears as

$$
\begin{array}{r|rrl}
1 & 2 & -3 & +3 \\
  &   & +2 & -1 \\
\hline
  & 2 & -1 & \;\;+2 = C \\
\end{array}
$$

showing the quotient $(2x - 1)$ and the remainder $2 = C$.

Our preceding equation now becomes

$$2x^2 - 3x + 3 = A(x-1)(x-2) + B(x-1) + 2$$

which reduces to

$$2x - 1 = A(x-2) + B$$

If now in this last equation we let $x = 2$ we find $B = 3$ which is the remainder when $(2x - 1)$ is divided by $(x - 2)$. By synthetic division the work appears as

$$
\begin{array}{r|rl}
2 & 2 & -1 \\
  &   & 4 \\
\hline
  & 2 & \;\;3 = B \\
\end{array}
$$

The preceding equation may now be written

$$2x - 1 = A(x-2) + 3 \quad \text{or} \quad 2(x-2) = A(x-2)$$

from which we obtain $A = 2$.

We can arrange the several synthetic divisions in compact form as follows:

$$
\begin{array}{r|rrr|r}
1 & 2 & -3 & +3 & -10 = D \\
  & 0 & 2 & -1 & \\
\hline
2 & 2 & -1 & +2 & = C \\
  & 0 & +4 & & \\
\hline
  & 2 & +3 & & = B \\
  & 0 & & & \\
\hline
  & 2 & & & = A
\end{array}
$$

We thus have

$$2x^3 - 3x^2 + 3x - 10 = 2x^{(3)} + 3x^{(2)} + 2x^{(1)} - 10$$

The values $A = 2$ and $D = -10$ could have been found immediately by equating coefficients of like powers in our given equation.

Newton's Theorem shows that it is possible to represent a polynomial of degree n by a series of factorial expressions. The coefficients, it will be recalled, are expressed in terms of U_0 and its leading differences and the determination of these requires a difference table. The synthetic division process is faster. Let us demonstrate the generality of this method.

Let $P_n(x)$ represent a polynomial of degree n:

$$P_n(x) = b_0 x^n + b_1 x^{n-1} + b_2 x^{n-2} + \cdots + b_{n-1} x + b_n \qquad (1)$$

By Newton's Theorem we can represent $P_n(x)$ by the expression

$$P_n(x) = A_0 + A_1 x + A_2 x(x - 1) + A_3 x(x - 1)(x - 2)$$
$$+ \cdots + A_n x(x - 1)(x - 2) \cdots (x - n + 1) \qquad (2)$$

We want to determine A_i, $i = 0, 1, 2, \cdots, n$, by a repetitive synthetic division process.

Divide $P_n(x)$ in (2) by x. The remainder is $A_0 = P_n(0) = b_n$ and the quotient is

$$P_{n-1}(x) = A_1 + A_2(x - 1) + A_3(x - 1)(x - 2) +$$
$$\cdots + A_n(x - 1)(x - 2) \cdots (x - n + 1)$$

Divide $P_{n-1}(x)$ by $(x - 1)$. The remainder is $P_{n-1}(1) = A_1$, and the quotient is

$$P_{n-2}(x) = A_2 + A_3(x - 2) + \cdots + A_n(x - 2)(x - 3) \cdots (x - n + 1)$$

Continuing this process we obtain finally

$$P_1(x) = A_{n-1} + A_n(x - n + 1)$$

Dividing $P_1(x)$ by $(x - n + 1)$ we obtain the remainder $A_{n-1} = P_1(n - 1)$ and the quotient A_n. This quotient A_n is however b_0, the coefficient of x^n in $P_n(x)$. Since the quantities $P_n(0)$, $P_{n-1}(1)$, $P_{n-2}(2)$, $\cdots$, $P_1(n - 1)$ are the remainders obtained when the polynomials $P_i(x)$, $i = n, n - 1, \cdots, 1$ are divided by $x, x - 1, x - 2, \cdots, x - n + 1$ respectively, therefore the coefficients $A_0, A_1, \cdots, A_{n-1}$ may be obtained by the repetitive synthetic division process. By equating the coefficients of the terms of highest degree in the two forms of $P_n(x)$, A_n can be determined.

Exercises

1. Find a polynomial U_x for which $U_0 = 3$, $U_1 = 14$, $U_2 = 40$, $U_3 = 86$, $U_4 = 157$, $U_5 = 258$.
2. Find the function U_x such that $\Delta U_x = x^3 + 3x^2 + 5x + 12$.
3. Represent the function $U_x = 11x^4 + 5x^3 + 2x^2 + x - 15$ and its differences in the factorial notation.
4. Prove by induction: $U_{x+n} = U_x + n\Delta U_x + \dfrac{n^{(2)}}{2!} \Delta^2 U_x + \cdots + \Delta^n U_x$.

5. Show that $\Delta^n \sin (a + bx) = \left(2 \sin \dfrac{b}{2} \right)^n \sin \left[a + bx + \dfrac{n(b + \pi)}{2} \right]$.

6. Show that $\Delta^n \cos (a + bx) = \left(2 \sin \dfrac{b}{2} \right)^n \cos \left[a + bx + \dfrac{n(b + \pi)}{2} \right]$.

7. Show that

(a) $\Delta(5x^4 + 6x^3 + x^2 - x + 7) = 20x^{(3)} + 108x^{(2)} + 108x + 11$.
(b) $\Delta(2x^4 - 7x^3 + 14x^2 - 25x + 7) = 8x^{(3)} + 15x^{(2)} + 14x - 16$.

8. Prove: $\Delta(U_x V_x) = U_{x+1}\Delta V_x + V_x\Delta U_x$.
9. Find ΔU_x if

(a) $U_x = 2^x \sin \dfrac{a}{2^x}$.   (b) $U_x = \tan \dfrac{a}{2^x}$.

10. Prove: $\Delta \left(\dfrac{U_x}{V_x} \right) = \dfrac{V_x\Delta U_x - U_x\Delta V_x}{V_x V_{x+1}}$.

11. Express $5x^3 - 11x^2 + 10x - 2$ in the form $A(x - 1)^3 + B(x - 1)^2 + C(x - 1) + D$ by the method of this section.

12. Show by induction $\Delta^n \dfrac{1}{x} = \dfrac{(-1)^n n!}{x^{[n+1]}}$.

13. Prove: $\Delta^m \begin{pmatrix} x \\ n \end{pmatrix} = \begin{pmatrix} x \\ n-m \end{pmatrix}$, $m < n$.

14. Prove: $x^{(n)} = x^{(m)}(x-m)^{(n-m)}$, $n > m$. Discuss when $m = 0$. What value should we give to $x^{(0)}$?

4. Symbolic Operators

In our defining equation

$$\Delta U_x = U_{x+1} - U_x$$

we have the fundamental relation connecting the first difference of a function with two successive values of that function. It is convenient to call Δ an *operator* that denotes the *operation* of taking the increment of the function to which it is prefixed; that is, when applied to U_x it produces $U_{x+1} - U_x$. If we write the preceding equation in the form

$$U_{x+1} = U_x + \Delta U_x = (1 + \Delta)U_x$$

the symbol $(1 + \Delta)$ is an operator which, when attached to a function, increases the value of the function by its increment.

The history of many of our theorems enlightens us about the progressive methods employed in their derivations. The theorems are usually observed to be true for particular cases and are then established in general by the method of mathematical induction. It is then frequently observed that the theorems are consequences of certain *formal laws of operation* or the application of *symbolic operators*.

If then we desire to employ *symbolic operators* in our work, we must establish the formal laws of operation which govern their use. Once it is established that the symbols of operation obey the ordinary algebraical laws, they may be separated from the functional symbols to which they are attached and may be treated as symbols of quantity.

For example, by defining $(1 + \Delta)^n U_x$ by the equation $(1 + \Delta)^n U_x = (1 + \Delta)[(1 + \Delta)^{n-1} U_x]$, n an integer, we can establish that

$$(1 + \Delta)^n U_x = U_x + n\Delta U_x + \frac{n^{(2)}}{2!} \Delta^2 U_x + \frac{n^{(3)}}{3!} \Delta^3 U_x + \cdots + \Delta^n U_x$$

$$= \left(1 + n\Delta + \frac{n^{(2)}}{2!} \Delta^2 + \cdots + \Delta^n\right) U_x$$

That is, the result is the same as if we found $(1 + \Delta)^n$ by the binomial theorem and then multiplied by U_x.

We have

$$(1 + \Delta)U_x = U_x + \Delta U_x$$

$$(1 + \Delta)^2 U_x = (1 + \Delta)[(1 + \Delta)U_x] = (1 + \Delta)[U_x + \Delta U_x]$$
$$= (U_x + \Delta U_x) + \Delta(U_x + \Delta U_x)$$
$$= U_x + 2\Delta U_x + \Delta^2 U_x$$

Similarly,

$$(1 + \Delta)^3 U_x = (1 + \Delta)[(1 + \Delta)^2 U_x] = (1 + \Delta)[U_x + 2\Delta U_x + \Delta^2 U_x]$$
$$= (U_x + 2\Delta U_x + \Delta^2 U_x) + \Delta(U_x + 2\Delta U_x + \Delta^2 U_x)$$
$$= U_x + 3\Delta U_x + 3\Delta^2 U_x + \Delta^3 U_x$$

By induction, it easily follows that

$$(1 + \Delta)^n U_x = U_x + n\Delta U_x + \frac{n^{(2)}}{2!}\Delta^2 U_x + \cdots + \Delta^n U_x$$

The study of finite differences is greatly facilitated by the introduction of another symbol E which denotes the operation of increasing the independent variable. Thus

$$\underset{h}{E}U_x = U_{x+h}$$

Inasmuch as we are assuming $h = 1$, we shall write

$$EU_x = U_{x+1}$$

Since

$$U_{x+1} = U_x + \Delta U_x = (1 + \Delta)U_x$$

it is evident that the operators E and Δ are connected by the relation [3]

$$E \equiv 1 + \Delta \quad \text{or} \quad \Delta \equiv E - 1$$

By repeating the operation E we have

$$E^2 U_x = E[EU_x] = EU_{x+1} = U_{x+2}$$
$$E^3 U_x = E[E^2 U_x] = EU_{x+2} = U_{x+3}$$

and in general

$$E^n U_x = U_{x+n}$$

We thus have the important Theorem 8.

Theorem 8.

$$U_{x+n} \equiv E^n U_x \equiv (1 + \Delta)^n U_x = \sum_{i=0}^{n} \frac{n^{(i)}}{i!}\Delta^i U_x, \quad 0! = n^{(0)} = \Delta^0 = 1$$

[3] The sign $\equiv$ should be read "is symbolically equivalent to."

We are acquainted with D as the symbol for the derivative. By means of Taylor's Series we can show the relation of the symbols E and D. If $D^n U_x$ represents the nth derivative of U_x, Taylor's Series is given by

$$U_{x+a} = U_x + aDU_x + \frac{a^2}{2!} D^2 U_x + \cdots + \frac{a^n}{n!} D^n U_x + \cdots$$

If $a = 1$, we have

$$U_{x+1} = EU_x = U_x + DU_x + \frac{D^2}{2!} U_x + \cdots + \frac{D^n}{n!} U_x + \cdots$$

which, when written symbolically, becomes

$$EU_x \equiv \left(1 + D + \frac{D^2}{2!} + \cdots + \frac{D^n}{n!} + \cdots \right) U_x$$

$$\equiv e^D U_x$$

We thus have the symbolic equivalence

$$E \equiv e^D$$

It thus appears that E, Δ, and D are connected by the relation

$$E \equiv 1 + \Delta \equiv e^D$$

From this, we immediately obtain

$$D \equiv \log E \equiv \log (1 + \Delta)$$

$$\Delta \equiv e^D - 1 \equiv E - 1$$

Many of the laws governing the use of the symbol Δ have been proved in the preceding section. We shall recapitulate them here and derive other laws not hitherto mentioned.[4]

1. $\Delta^n (U_x + V_x - W_x) = \Delta^n U_x + \Delta^n V_x - \Delta^n W_x$
2. $\Delta^n c U_x = c \Delta^n U_x$
3. $\Delta^m \Delta^n U_x = \Delta^{m+n} U_x$
4. $E^n (U_x + V_x - W_x) = E^n U_x + E^n V_x - E^n W_x$
5. $E^n c U_x = c E^n U_x$
6. $E^m E^n U_x = E^{m+n} U_x$
7. $EU_x V_x = EU_x EV_x$
8. $E^n U_x = \sum_{r=0}^{n} \binom{n}{r} \Delta^r U_x, \quad \binom{n}{0} = \Delta^0 = 1$

Thus, in many respects the symbols E, Δ, and D behave like algebraic symbols of quantity. They can be separated from the symbols represent-

[4] At the present, m and n are tacitly assumed to be positive integers.

ing the functions to which they belong provided they are ultimately read in connection with the symbol denoting the function to which they refer and are interpreted as symbols of operation. This principle is known as the Law of Separation of Symbols.

Defining $\dfrac{1}{E} U_x = E^{-1}U_x$ as that expression which, when operated upon by E, produces U_x, we find $\dfrac{1}{E^n} U_x = E^{-n}U_x = U_{x-n}$.

Examples.

$$E(x^2 + \sin x) = (x + 1)^2 + \sin (x + 1)$$

$$E(a^x + \log \sin x) = a^{x+1} + \log \sin (x + 1)$$

If $EU_x = x + \sin x$, $U_x = (x - 1) + \sin (x - 1)$, and if $E^n U_x = F(x)$, $U_x = F(x - n)$.

Exercises

By separation of symbols in 1 to 5:

1. Show that $DU_x = \Delta U_x - \dfrac{\Delta^2 U_x}{2} + \dfrac{\Delta^3 U_x}{3} - \cdots$.

2. Show that $\Delta^n e^x = e^{x+n} - ne^{x+n-1} + \dfrac{n(n-1)}{2!} e^{x+n-2} + \cdots + (-1)^n e^x$.

3. Show that $U_{x+n} = U_x + nDU_x + \dfrac{n^2}{2!} D^2 U_x + \cdots$.

4. Show that $\Delta^n U_x = U_{x+n} - nU_{x+n-1} + \dfrac{n^{(2)}}{2!} U_{x+n-2} - \dfrac{n^{(3)}}{3!} U_{x+n-3} + \cdots + (-1)^n U_x$.

5. Show that $U_{x+n} = U_x + n\Delta U_x + \dfrac{n^{(2)}}{2!} \Delta^2 U_x + \cdots + \Delta^n U_x$.

6. Show that if $f(E)$ is a polynomial in E, $f(E)a^x = a^x f(a)$.

Chapter II

FINITE INTEGRATION AND APPLICATIONS

1. Finite Integration

In finite differences the term integration is used to denote the process of finding a function V_x whose difference is a given function U_x. That is, we wish to determine V_x so that

$$\Delta V_x = U_x$$

U_x being a given function of x.

The operation is therefore the inverse of that denoted by Δ and it may be denoted by Δ^{-1} or $1/\Delta$, just as ordinary integration may be denoted by D^{-1} or $1/D$.

The quantity V_x whose difference is U_x may be indicated by the equation

$$V_x = \Delta^{-1} U_x$$

and $\Delta^{-1} U_x$ may be called the indefinite finite integral of U_x.

To illustrate, we have learned that

$$\Delta \frac{x^{(3)}}{3} = x^{(2)}$$

so inversely we have

$$\Delta^{-1} x^{(2)} = \frac{x^{(3)}}{3}$$

and we say that $\dfrac{x^{(3)}}{3}$ is a finite integral of $x^{(2)}$.

We have learned that a constant term or a periodic function of period 1 disappears in differencing. Consequently, in the process of integration, a quantity C whose difference is 0 is added.[1]   Thus

$$\Delta^{-1}x^{(2)} = \frac{x^{(3)}}{3} + C$$

for

$$\Delta \left[\frac{x^{(3)}}{3} + C \right] = x^{(2)}$$

Hence, we write

$$\Delta^{-1}U_x = V_x + C$$

where

$$\Delta(V_x + C) = U_x$$

Further, if

$$\Delta^{-1}U_x = V_x + C$$

or

$$\Delta(V_x + C) = U_x$$

we have

$$\Delta[\Delta^{-1}U_x] = \Delta(V_x + C) = U_x$$

That is, the operation Δ^{-1} upon a function followed by the operation Δ leaves the function unchanged.   However, the operators Δ and Δ^{-1} are not commutative.   Observe that $\Delta^{-1}[\Delta U_x]$ may not give U_x.   Thus

$$\Delta^{-1}\left[\Delta \frac{x^{(3)}}{3} \right] = \Delta^{-1}x^{(2)} = \frac{x^{(3)}}{3} + C$$

whereas

$$\Delta \left[\Delta^{-1}\frac{x^{(3)}}{3} \right] = \Delta \left[\frac{x^{(4)}}{12} + C \right] = \frac{x^{(3)}}{3}$$

Inasmuch as our knowledge of the value of $\Delta^{-1}U_x$ is almost always obtained from our previous knowledge of the results of the operation Δ, it would be the part of wisdom to tabulate those finite integrals that may be immediately obtained from well-known differences. We tabulate the differences and corresponding finite integrals in Table 5. Obviously a quantity C should be added to each finite integral.

[1] If the variable x is discontinuous, C is a constant; if continuous, C may be a periodic function of period 1.

TABLE 5

Finite Differences	*Finite Integrals*

1. $\Delta(U_x + V_x - W_x)$
$$= \Delta U_x + \Delta V_x - \Delta W_x$$

$\Delta^{-1}(U_x + V_x - W_x)$
$$= \Delta^{-1}U_x + \Delta^{-1}V_x - \Delta^{-1}W_x$$

2. $\Delta kU_x = k\Delta U_x$

$\Delta^{-1}kU_x = k\Delta^{-1}U_x$

3. $\Delta a^x = (a-1)a^x$

$\Delta^{-1}a^x = \dfrac{a^x}{a-1}, \; a \neq 1$

4. $\Delta x^{(n)} = nx^{(n-1)}$

$\Delta^{-1}x^{(n)} = \dfrac{x^{(n+1)}}{n+1}$

5. $\Delta \dfrac{1}{x^{|n|}} = \dfrac{-n}{x^{|n+1|}}$

$\Delta^{-1}\dfrac{1}{x^{|n|}} = \dfrac{1}{(1-n)x^{|n-1|}}, \; n \neq 1$

6. $\Delta(a+bx)^{(n)} = bn(a+bx)^{(n-1)}$

$\Delta^{-1}(a+bx)^{(n)} = \dfrac{(a+bx)^{(n+1)}}{b(n+1)}$

7. $\Delta \dfrac{1}{(a+bx)^{|n|}} = \dfrac{-bn}{(a+bx)^{|n+1|}}$

$\Delta^{-1}\dfrac{1}{(a+bx)^{|n|}} = \dfrac{1}{b(1-n)(a+bx)^{|n-1|}}$

8. $\Delta \sin(a+bx)$
$$= 2\sin\frac{b}{2}\cos\left(a+\frac{b}{2}+bx\right)$$

$\Delta^{-1}\cos(a+bx)$
$$= \frac{1}{2\sin\dfrac{b}{2}}\sin\left(a-\frac{b}{2}+bx\right)$$

9. $\Delta \cos(a+bx)$
$$= -2\sin\frac{b}{2}\sin\left(a+\frac{b}{2}+bx\right)$$

$\Delta^{-1}\sin(a+bx)$
$$= \frac{-1}{2\sin\dfrac{b}{2}}\cos\left(a-\frac{b}{2}+bx\right)$$

10. $\Delta\binom{x}{n} = \binom{x}{n-1}$

$\Delta^{-1}\binom{x}{n} = \binom{x}{n+1}$

11. $\Delta U_x V_x = U_x\Delta V_x + V_{x+1}\Delta U_x$

$\Delta^{-1}[U_x\Delta V_x] = U_x V_x - \Delta^{-1}[V_{x+1}\Delta U_x]$

12. $\Delta x! = x(x!)$

$\Delta^{-1}x(x!) = x!$

13. $\Delta \tan(a+bx)$
$$= \frac{\sin b}{\cos(a+bx)\cos(a+b+bx)}$$

$\Delta^{-1}\sec(a+bx)\sec(a+b+bx)$
$$= \csc b \tan(a+bx)$$

14. $\Delta \cot(a+bx)$
$$= \frac{-\sin b}{\sin(a+bx)\sin(a+b+bx)}$$

$\Delta^{-1}\csc(a+bx)\csc(a+b+bx)$
$$= -\csc b \cot(a+bx)$$

15. $\Delta \sec(a+bx)$
$$= \frac{2\sin\dfrac{b}{2}\sin\left(a+\dfrac{b}{2}+bx\right)}{\cos(a+bx)\cos(a+b+bx)}$$

$\Delta^{-1}\dfrac{\sin\left(a+\dfrac{b}{2}+bx\right)}{\cos(a+bx)\cos(a+b+bx)}$
$$= \frac{\sec(a+bx)}{2\sin\dfrac{b}{2}}$$

16. $\Delta \csc(a+bx)$
$$= \frac{-2\sin\dfrac{b}{2}\cos\left(a+\dfrac{b}{2}+bx\right)}{\sin(a+bx)\sin(a+b+bx)}$$

$\Delta^{-1}\dfrac{\cos\left(a+\dfrac{b}{2}+bx\right)}{\sin(a+bx)\sin(a+b+bx)}$
$$= \frac{-\csc(a+bx)}{2\sin\dfrac{b}{2}}$$

Example 1. Find the finite integral: $\Delta^{-1}3^x$.

Using formula 3 of the integrals of Table 5 we have

$$\Delta^{-1}3^x = \frac{3^x}{3-1} + C = \frac{3^x}{2} + C$$

Example 2. Find the finite integral: $\Delta^{-1}(x^3 - 2x^2 + 7x - 12)$.

To solve this problem we first express $(x^3 - 2x^2 + 7x - 12)$ as a series of factorials; then we apply formulas 1, 2, and 4 of the integrals of Table 5.

1	1	-2	$+7$	-12
	0	$+1$	-1	
2	1	-1	$+6$	
	0	2		
	1	$+1$		
	0			
	1			

$$x^3 - 2x^2 + 7x - 12 \equiv x^{(3)} + x^{(2)} + 6x^{(1)} - 12$$

$$\Delta^{-1}(x^3 - 2x^2 + 7x - 12 = \Delta^{-1}(x^{(3)} + x^{(2)} + 6x^{(1)} - 12)$$

$$= \Delta^{-1}x^{(3)} + \Delta^{-1}x^{(2)} + 6\Delta^{-1}x^{(1)} - 12\Delta^{-1}x^{(0)}$$

$$= \frac{x^{(4)}}{4} + \frac{x^{(3)}}{3} + 3x^{(2)} - 12x^{(1)} + C$$

Example 3. Find the finite integral: $\Delta^{-1}[x(x + 1)(x + 2)]$.

Here we note that

$$x(x + 1)(x + 2) = (x + 2)^{(3)} = (a + bx)^{(3)} \quad \text{if } a = 2, b = 1, n = 3.$$

Hence, applying formula 6 of the integrals in Table 5 we have

$$\Delta^{-1}[x(x + 1)(x + 2)] = \Delta^{-1}(2 + x)^{(3)}$$

$$= \frac{(2 + x)^{(4)}}{4} + C$$

$$= \frac{(x + 2)(x + 1)(x)(x - 1)}{4} + C$$

Exercises

Find the following finite integrals:

1. $\Delta^{-1}(x^3 + 2x^2 - 8x + 9)$.

2. $\Delta^{-1}[x(x + 2)(x + 3)]$ by two methods.

    Hint: $x(x + 2)(x + 3) = (x + 1 - 1)(x + 2)(x + 3) = (x + 3)^{(3)} = (x + 3)^{(2)}$.

3. $\Delta^{-1}x^2$.

4. $\Delta^{-1}x^3$.

5. $\Delta^{-1}[x(x + 2)(x + 4)]$ by two methods.

6. $\Delta^{-1}[(2x + 1)(2x + 3)]$ by two methods.

7. $\Delta^{-1}\dfrac{1}{x^{|2|}}$.

8. $\Delta^{-1}\dfrac{1}{(3 + 2x)^{|4|}}$.

9. $\Delta^{-1}\dfrac{1}{x^2 - 1}$.

10. $\Delta^{-1}\dfrac{1}{(2x - 1)(2x + 1)(2x + 5)}$.

11. $\Delta^{-1}\dfrac{1}{1 + 2 + 3 + \cdots + x}$.

12. $\Delta^{-1}\dfrac{x + 3}{x(x + 1)(x + 2)}$.

13. $\Delta^{-1}\sin(2x + 3)$.

14. $\Delta^{-1}[x(x + a)(x + 2a)]$.

15. $\Delta^{-1}[(x - a)(x - b)]$.

16. $\Delta^{-1}\sin^2(a + bx)$.

17. $\Delta^{-1}\cos^2(a + bx)$.

18. $\Delta^{-1}\dfrac{1}{2^x}\tan\dfrac{\theta}{2^x} = \dfrac{1}{2^{x-1}}\cot\dfrac{\theta}{2^{x-1}}$.

19. $\Delta^{-1}\left(2^x \sin^2\dfrac{\theta}{2^x}\right)^2 = \left(2^{x-1}\sin\dfrac{\theta}{2^{x-1}}\right)^2$.

20. $\Delta^{-1} - \left(\dfrac{1}{2^x}\sec\dfrac{\theta}{2^x}\right)^2 = \left(\dfrac{1}{2^{x-1}}\csc\dfrac{\theta}{2^{x-1}}\right)^2$.

21. Show that $\Delta^{-1} \dfrac{c^x[Ax^2 + Bx + D]}{x(x+1)} = \dfrac{c^x(ax+b)}{x}$ if $a = \dfrac{A}{c-1}$; $b = -D$.

22. $\Delta^{-1} \csc 2^x\theta = -\cot 2^{x-1}\theta$.

23. $\Delta^{-1} 2^x \tan 2^x\theta = -2^x \cot 2^x\theta$.

24. $\Delta^{-1} 2^x \sin \dfrac{\theta}{2^x} \left(\sin \dfrac{\theta}{2^{x+1}}\right)^2 = 2^{x-2} \sin \dfrac{\theta}{2^{x-1}}$.

25. $\Delta^{-1} \arctan \dfrac{1}{1+x+x^2} = \arctan x$.

26. $\Delta^{-1} \dfrac{1}{2^x} \log \tan 2^x\theta = -\dfrac{1}{2^{x-1}} \log (2 \sin 2^x\theta)$.

27. $\Delta^{-1} \sinh (a + bx) = \dfrac{\cosh \left(a - \dfrac{b}{2} + bx\right)}{2 \sinh \dfrac{b}{2}}$.

28. $\Delta^{-1} \cosh (a + bx) = \dfrac{\sinh \left(a - \dfrac{b}{2} + bx\right)}{2 \sinh \dfrac{b}{2}}$.

2. Summation of Series

A very important application of the calculus of finite differences is to the problem of finding a compact formula for the sum of n terms of a given series. It is easily seen, as we shall presently show, that the summation problem is in reality the problem of finite integration.

Let V_x be a function whose difference is U_x. That is

$$\Delta V_x = U_x \quad \text{or} \quad V_x = \Delta^{-1} U_x$$

Since the above equation means

$$V_{x+1} - V_x = U_x$$

we have

$$V_1 - V_0 = U_0$$
$$V_2 - V_1 = U_1$$
$$V_3 - V_2 = U_2$$
$$\cdot \quad \cdot \quad \cdot \quad \cdot \quad \cdot \quad \cdot \quad \cdot \quad \cdot$$
$$V_a - V_{a-1} = U_{a-1}$$
$$V_{a+1} - V_a = U_a$$
$$\cdot \quad \cdot \quad \cdot \quad \cdot \quad \cdot \quad \cdot \quad \cdot \quad \cdot$$
$$V_{n-1} - V_{n-2} = U_{n-2}$$
$$V_n - V_{n-1} = U_{n-1}$$
$$V_{n+1} - V_n = U_n$$

Adding, we have

$$U_0 + U_1 + U_2 + \cdots + U_n = \sum_0^n U_x = V_{n+1} - V_0 = V_x]_0^{n+1}$$

$$= \Delta^{-1} U_x]_0^{n+1}$$

and

$$U_0 + U_1 + U_2 + \cdots + U_{a-1} = \sum_0^{a-1} U_x = V_a - V_0 = V_x]_0^a$$

$$= \Delta^{-1} U_x]_0^a$$

and more generally

$$U_a + U_{a+1} + \cdots + U_n = \sum_a^n U_x = V_{n+1} - V_a = V_x]_a^{n+1}$$

$$= \Delta^{-1} U_x]_a^{n+1}$$

It is thus seen that the sum of any number of terms of a series of values of U_x is equal to the difference between two values of another function V_x that is the finite integral of U_x. Thus a sufficient condition for finding the sum $\sum_1^n U_x$ is to find a function V_x such that $\Delta V_x = U_x$. We call V_x $(= \Delta^{-1} U_x)$ the indefinite finite integral of U_x and when the definite limits are applied we have the definite finite integral of U_x. Thus

$$\Delta^{-1} U_x = V_x + C$$

is an indefinite integral, but

$$\sum_a^b U_x = V_{b+1} - V_a = V_x]_a^{b+1} = \Delta^{-1} U_x]_a^{b+1}$$

is a definite integral.

Example 1. Find the sum of the series $2 + 4 + 6 + \cdots + 2n$.

Solution: $U_x = 2x$.

$$\sum_1^n U_x = \Delta^{-1} 2x]_1^{n+1} = 2\Delta^{-1} x]_1^{n+1} = x^{(2)}]_1^{n+1}$$

$$= (n + 1)^{(2)} - 1^{(2)} = (n + 1)n - 1.0 = n(n + 1)$$

Example 2. Find the sum of the series

$$1 \cdot 2 + 2 \cdot 3 + 3 \cdot 4 + \cdots + n(n + 1)$$

Solution: $U_x = x(x + 1) = (1 + x)^{(2)} = (a + bx)^{(m)}$ when $a = 1$, $b = 1$, $m = 2$.

$$\sum_1^n U_x = \sum_1^n (1 + x)^{(2)} = \Delta^{-1}(1 + x)^{(2)}]_1^{n+1} = \frac{(1 + x)^{(3)}}{3}\Bigg]_1^{n+1}$$

$$= \frac{(n + 2)^{(3)}}{3} - \frac{2^{(3)}}{3} = \frac{1}{3}(n + 2)(n + 1)n$$

Example 3. Find the sum of the series

$$1^2 + 2^2 + 3^2 + \cdots + n^2$$

Solution: $U_x = x^2 = x(x-1) + x = x^{(2)} + x^{(1)}$.

$$\sum_1^n U_x = \Delta^{-1}[x^{(2)} + x^{(1)}]_1^{n+1} = \frac{x^{(3)}}{3} + \frac{x^{(2)}}{2}\Big]_1^{n+1}$$

$$= \frac{(n+1)^{(3)}}{3} + \frac{(n+1)^{(2)}}{2} = \frac{(n+1)n(n-1)}{3} + \frac{(n+1)n}{2}$$

$$= \frac{n(n+1)(2n+1)}{6}$$

Example 4. Find the sum of the first n terms of the series whose xth term is $(x^3 + 7x)$.

Solution: We express $U_x = x^3 + 7x$ as a series of factorials in which form $\Delta^{-1}U_x$ can be found. (See below.) We find

$$U_x = x^3 + 7x = x^{(3)} + 3x^{(2)} + 8x^{(1)}$$

$$\sum_1^n U_x = \Delta^{-1}[x^{(3)} + 3x^{(2)} + 8x^{(1)}]_1^{n+1}$$

$$= \frac{x^{(4)}}{4} + x^{(3)} + 4x^{(2)}]_1^{n+1}$$

$$= \frac{(n+1)^{(4)}}{4} + (n+1)^{(3)} + 4(n+1)^{(2)}$$

$$= \tfrac{1}{4}n(n+1)(n^2 + n + 14)$$

1	1	$+0$	$+7$	$+0$
	0	$+1$	$+1$	
2	1	$+1$	$+8$	
	0	$+2$		
	1	$+3$		
	0			
	1			

Exercises

Sum the following series:

1. (a) $1^3 + 2^3 + 3^3 + \cdots + n^3$;   (b) $1^4 + 2^4 + 3^4 + \cdots + n^4$.

2. $\dfrac{1^2}{1} + \dfrac{1^2 + 2^2}{2} + \dfrac{1^2 + 2^2 + 3^2}{3} + \cdots + \dfrac{1^2 + 2^2 + 3^2 + \cdots + n^2}{n}$.

3. $\dfrac{1}{1} + \dfrac{1}{1+2} + \dfrac{1}{1+2+3} + \cdots + \dfrac{1}{1+2+3+\cdots+n}$.

4. $1 \cdot 3 + 2 \cdot 4 + 3 \cdot 5 + \cdots + n(n+2)$.

5. $1 \cdot 2^2 + 2 \cdot 3^2 + 3 \cdot 4^2 + \cdots + n(n+1)^2$.

6. $\dfrac{1}{1 \cdot 2} + \dfrac{1}{2 \cdot 3} + \dfrac{1}{3 \cdot 4} + \cdots + \dfrac{1}{n(n+1)}$.   Also find $\lim\limits_{n \to \infty} \sum\limits_{1}^{n} U_x$.

7. $\dfrac{1}{1 \cdot 2 \cdot 3} + \dfrac{1}{2 \cdot 3 \cdot 4} + \dfrac{1}{3 \cdot 4 \cdot 5} + \cdots$ to n terms.

8. $\dfrac{1}{1 \cdot 4} + \dfrac{1}{4 \cdot 7} + \dfrac{1}{7 \cdot 10} + \cdots$ to n terms.

9. $\dfrac{1}{1 \cdot 2 \cdot 4} + \dfrac{1}{2 \cdot 3 \cdot 5} + \dfrac{1}{3 \cdot 4 \cdot 6} + \cdots + \dfrac{1}{n(n+1)(n+3)}$.

     Hint: $U_x = \dfrac{x+2}{x^{|4|}} = \dfrac{1}{(x+1)^{|3|}} + \dfrac{2}{x^{|4|}}$.

10. $12 + 40 + 90 + 168 + 280 + \cdots$ to n terms.

     Hint: Use Newton's Theorem to find U_x.

11. $6 \cdot 9 + 12 \cdot 21 + 20 \cdot 37 + 30 \cdot 57 + 42 \cdot 81 + \cdots$ to n terms.

     Hint: Apply Newton's Theorem twice and show that

$$U_x = (x^2 + 3x + 2)(2x^2 + 6x + 1)$$
$$= 2(3 + x)^{(4)} + (2 + x)^{(2)}$$

12. Show that $\sum\limits_{1}^{n-1} \sin \dfrac{\pi}{n} x = \cot \dfrac{\pi}{2n}$.

13. Show that $\sum\limits_{1}^{n} \left(2^x \sin^2 \dfrac{\theta}{2^x} \right)^2 = \left(2^n \sin \dfrac{\theta}{2^n} \right)^2 - \sin^2 \theta$.

14. Show that $\sum\limits_{1}^{n} \left(\dfrac{1}{2^x} \sec \dfrac{\theta}{2^x} \right)^2 = \csc^2 \theta - \left(\dfrac{1}{2^n} \csc \dfrac{\theta}{2^n} \right)^2$.

15. Show that $\sum\limits_{1}^{n} x(x!) = \Delta^{-1} x(x!) \Big]_{1}^{n+1} = (n+1)! - 1$.

16. Two railway trucks traveled 3 hours at 4 miles per hour; three trucks traveled 4 hours at 5 miles per hour; four trucks traveled 5 hours at 6 miles per hour; and so on until finally 28 trucks traveled 29 hours at 30 miles an hour. What was the total mileage covered by all the trucks?

17. Find $\sum\limits_{1}^{n} \csc 2^x \theta$.

18. Find $\sum\limits_{0}^{n-1} [\sin 3(2^{x-1}\theta) \sin 2^{x-1}\theta]$.

19. Find $\sum\limits_{0}^{n-1} [\tan 2^{x-1}\theta + \cot 2^{x-1}\theta]$.

20. Prove: $\sum\limits_{1}^{n} (x^2 + 1)x! = n(n + 1)!$.

21. Find the sum: $1 + 3(2!) + 7(3!) + 13(4!) + 21(5!) + \cdots$ to n terms.

22. Find the sum: $2 \cdot 2 + 7 \cdot 4 + 14 \cdot 8 + 23 \cdot 16 + 34 \cdot 32 + \cdots$ to n terms.

23. Find the sum: $4 + 5 + 8 + 15 + 30 + 61 + \cdots$ to n terms.

24. Find the sum: $2 + 5 + 20 + 71 + 230 + 713 + \cdots$ to n terms.

25. Differentiate with respect to θ both sides of the solution of Number 17,

$$\sum\limits_{1}^{n} \csc 2^x\theta = \cot\theta - \cot 2^n\theta \text{ and obtain}$$

$$\sum\limits_{1}^{n} 2^x \csc 2^x\theta \cot 2^x\theta = \csc^2\theta - 2^n \csc^2 2^n\theta.$$

3. MORE ADVANCED METHODS OF INTEGRATION

A. INTEGRATION BY PARTS

The method of integration by parts, or partial integration, is very useful for integrating certain types of functions.[2] The method is derived from the well-known formula for the difference of a product

$$\Delta U_x V_x = U_x \Delta V_x + V_{x+1} \Delta U_x$$

Transposing and integrating we have the formula for partial integration.

$$\Delta^{-1}[U_x \Delta V_x] = U_x V_x - \Delta^{-1}[V_{x+1}\Delta U_x]$$

This formula is applicable if we can determine V_x from ΔV_x and if we can find the finite integral $\Delta^{-1}[V_{x+1}\Delta U_x]$. We add the constant of integration at the completion of the process.

Example 1. Find the finite integral: $\Delta^{-1}x3^x$.

Solution: Let

$$U_x = x, \quad \Delta V_x = 3^x$$

then

$$\Delta U_x = 1, \quad V_x = \Delta^{-1}3^x = \frac{3^x}{2}$$

$$V_{x+1} = \frac{3^{x+1}}{2} = \frac{3}{2} \cdot 3^x$$

---

[2] Especially valuable for integrating products of two functions, one of which is transcendental.

Substituting in the formula for the partial integration,

$$\Delta^{-1}x3^x = x \cdot \frac{3^x}{2} - \Delta^{-1}\left[\frac{3}{2} \cdot 3^x \cdot 1\right] + C$$

$$= x\frac{3^x}{2} - \frac{3}{2} \cdot \Delta^{-1}3^x + C$$

$$= x\frac{3^x}{2} - \frac{3}{2} \cdot \frac{3^x}{2} + C = 3^x\left[\frac{x}{2} - \frac{3}{4}\right] + C$$

Exercises

Sum the series:

1. $1^2 \cdot 2 + 2^2 \cdot 2^2 + 3^2 \cdot 2^3 + 4^2 \cdot 2^4 + \cdots + n^2 2^n$.

2. $2 \cdot 2 + 6 \cdot 2^2 + 12 \cdot 2^3 + 20 \cdot 2^4 + 30 \cdot 2^5 + \cdots$ to n terms.

3. $\sum_{1}^{n} x \sin x$.

4. If U_x is a rational integral function of degree n, show that continued repetition of the method of partial integration gives

$$\Delta^{-1}a^x U_x =$$

$$\frac{a^x}{a-1}\left[U_x - \frac{a}{a-1}\Delta U_x + \left(\frac{a}{a-1}\right)^2\Delta^2 U_x + \cdots + (-1)^n\left(\frac{a}{a-1}\right)^n\Delta^n U_x\right]$$

5. Apply Number 4 above to find $\sum_{1}^{n} 3^x x^{(2)}$.

6. Apply Number 4 above to find $\sum_{1}^{n} 2^x(x^3 - 3x + 2)$.

7. Use the method of partial integration to sum the series $\dfrac{1}{1 \cdot 2 \cdot 4} + \dfrac{1}{2 \cdot 3 \cdot 5} + \dfrac{1}{3 \cdot 4 \cdot 6}$ $+ \cdots$ to n terms.

8. Find $\sum_{1}^{n} \dfrac{1}{(5x-2)(5x+3)}$.

9. Find $\sum_{1}^{n} \dfrac{ax+b}{x^{|3|}}$.

10. Find $\sum_{2}^{n} \dfrac{1}{x^2-1}$.

11. Find $\sum_{1}^{n} \dfrac{1}{(2n-1)(2n+1)(2n+5)}$.

12. Find the sum of the infinite series: $\dfrac{1 \cdot 2}{3} + \dfrac{2 \cdot 3}{3^2} + \dfrac{3 \cdot 4}{3^3} + \dfrac{4 \cdot 5}{3^4} + \cdots$.

B. THE METHOD OF UNDETERMINED COEFFICIENTS AND UNDETERMINED
FUNCTIONS

When the quantity V_x (= $\Delta^{-1} U_x$) cannot be referred to any of the preceding forms given in Table 5, it is often possible to conjecture the form of V_x from a general knowledge of the effects of the operator Δ.

We have noted that the operator Δ converts polynomials into polynomials, exponential functions into exponential functions, trigonometric functions into trigonometric functions, and so on.

Due to the fact that the operator Δ does not alter the functional characteristics, the limits of conjecture are narrowed.

We shall illustrate this method by a few examples.

Example 1.   Find the finite integral $\Delta^{-1} \dfrac{x2^x}{(x+1)(x+2)}$.

Solution: We wish to find V_x such that

$$\Delta V_x = U_x = \frac{x2^x}{(x+1)(x+2)}$$

From our knowledge of differencing we assume

$$V_x = \frac{f(x)}{x+1} 2^x$$

where $f(x)$ is an undetermined rational integral function of x.

Since

$$\Delta V_x = V_{x+1} - V_x = U_x$$

we have

$$\frac{f(x+1)2^{x+1}}{x+2} - \frac{f(x)2^x}{x+1} = \frac{x2^x}{(x+1)(x+2)}$$

or

$$2(x+1)f(x+1) - (x+2)f(x) = x$$

Now the right-hand side of this equation is linear. It is evident that in order that the left-hand side be linear, the undetermined function $f(x)$ should be constant. Call the constant k. We then have

$$f(x) = k$$

$$f(x+1) = k$$

and

$$2(x+1)k - (x+2)k = x$$

from which

$$kx = x$$

$$k = 1 = f(x)$$

$$\therefore \Delta^{-1} \frac{x2^x}{(x+1)(x+2)} = \frac{1}{(x+1)} \cdot 2^x + C$$

Example 2. Find the sum of n terms of the series whose xth term is $\dfrac{x2^x}{(x+2)!}$.

Solution: We wish to find V_x such that

$$\Delta V_x = U_x = \frac{x2^x}{(x+2)!}$$

From our knowledge of differencing we assume

$$V_x = \frac{f(x)2^x}{(x+1)!}$$

where $f(x)$ is an undetermined rational integral function of x.

Since

$$\Delta V_x = V_{x+1} - V_x = U_x$$

we have

$$\frac{f(x+1) \cdot 2^{x+1}}{(x+2)!} - \frac{f(x) \cdot 2^x}{(x+1)!} = \frac{x2^x}{(x+2)!}$$

or

$$2f(x+1) - (x+2)f(x) = x$$

Since the right-hand side of this equation is of the first degree, it is evident that the left-hand side will be of the first degree when $f(x)$ is a constant. We then have

$$f(x) = k$$

$$f(x+1) = k$$

and, substituting in the preceding equation,

$$2k - (x+2)k = x$$

from which

$$k = -1$$

Hence

$$V_x = \frac{-1 \cdot 2^x}{(x+1)!}$$

and

$$\sum_{1}^{n} U_x = \sum_{1}^{n} \frac{x2^x}{(x+2)!} = \Delta^{-1} \frac{x2^x}{(x+2)!}\Big]_1^{n+1} = \frac{-2^x}{(x+1)!}\Big]_1^{n+1}$$

$$= 1 - \frac{2^{n+1}}{(n+2)!}$$

Example 3. Find the finite integral $\Delta^{-1} \dfrac{2x-1}{2^{x-1}}$.

Solution: Let $\Delta^{-1} \dfrac{2x-1}{2^{x-1}} = V_x = \dfrac{f(x)}{2^{x-1}}$.

Then, since

$$\Delta V_x = U_x$$

$$\frac{f(x+1)}{2^x} - \frac{f(x)}{2^{x-1}} = \frac{2x-1}{2^{x-1}}$$

or

$$f(x+1) - 2f(x) = 4x - 2$$

Evidently $f(x)$ must be a linear function of x. Then if

$$f(x) = ax + b$$

$$f(x+1) = a(x+1) + b = ax + a + b$$

Substituting, we have

$$(ax + a + b) - 2(ax + b) = 4x - 2$$

Equating coefficients, we obtain

$$ax - 2ax = 4x$$

$$a + b - 2b = -2$$

from which

$$a = -4$$

$$b = -2$$

and

$$f(x) = -4x - 2$$

We now obtain

$$V_x = \frac{-4x - 2}{2^{x-1}} = -\frac{2x+1}{2^{x-2}}$$

that is,

$$\Delta^{-1} \frac{2x-1}{2^{x-1}} = -\frac{2x+1}{2^{x-2}} + C$$

Exercises

Sum the following series:

1. $\dfrac{9}{1\cdot2\cdot3}\left(\dfrac{3}{4}\right) + \dfrac{10}{2\cdot3\cdot4}\left(\dfrac{3}{4}\right)^2 + \dfrac{11}{3\cdot4\cdot5}\left(\dfrac{3}{4}\right)^3 + \cdots + \dfrac{n+8}{n^{|3|}}\left(\dfrac{3}{4}\right)^n.$

2. The series whose nth term is $\dfrac{n+2}{n^{|2|}}\left(\dfrac{1}{2}\right)^n.$

3. The series whose nth term is $\dfrac{n+14}{n^{|3|}}\left(\dfrac{6}{7}\right)^n.$

4. $\dfrac{3}{2\cdot5\cdot8} + \dfrac{5}{5\cdot8\cdot11} + \dfrac{7}{8\cdot11\cdot14} + \cdots + \dfrac{2n+1}{(3n-1)^{|3|}}.$

5. Show that in order to sum the series ΣU_x where $U_x = \dfrac{a+bx}{x^{|n|}}\cdot r^x$, it is necessary that $r = 1 - (n-1)\dfrac{b}{a}.$

6. Find $\displaystyle\sum_1^n U_x$ where $U_x = \dfrac{x}{(x+1)(x+2)}\,2^x.$

7. Find $\displaystyle\sum_0^{n-1} U_x$ if $U_x = \sin(a+bx).$

8. Find $\displaystyle\sum_0^{n-1} U_x$ if $U_x = \cos(a+bx).$

9. Develop the formula for $\Delta^{-1}\dfrac{cx+d}{(a+bx)^{|n|}}.$

10. Apply the result of Number 9 to find $\Delta^{-1}\dfrac{3x+5}{(1+2x)^{|3|}}.$

11. Find $\displaystyle\lim_{n\to\infty}\sum_1^n \dfrac{2x-1}{2^{x-1}}.$

12. Find $\displaystyle\lim_{n\to\infty}\sum_1^n \dfrac{x+2}{x^{|2|}2^x}.$

13. Find $\displaystyle\lim_{n\to\infty}\sum_2^n \dfrac{1}{x^2-1}.$

14. Find $\displaystyle\sum_1^n x(x+2)(x+4).$

15. Find $\displaystyle\sum_1^n \dfrac{x^2+2x+1}{x^2+2x}.$

16. Show that $\Delta^{-1}\dfrac{(a+bx)R^x}{(c+dx)^{|n|}} = \dfrac{kR^x}{(c+dx)^{|n-1|}},$ where $k = \dfrac{b}{d(R-1)},$

provided $R - 1 = \dfrac{bd(n-1)}{bc-ad}.$

17. Find by two methods $\displaystyle\sum_1^n U_x$ when $U_x = r^x \sin(a+bx).$

18. Find by two methods $\displaystyle\sum_1^n U_x$ when $U_x = r^x \cos(a+bx).$

19. Find $\sum_1^n U_x$ when $U_x = \dfrac{x^2 + x - 1}{(x + 2)!}$.

20. Find $\Delta^{-1}\left[2^x \cdot x \cdot \dfrac{x!}{(2x + 1)!}\right]$.

21. Find $\sum_0^n \dfrac{(a + x)^2}{3^{a+x}}$.

22. Find $\sum_1^n \sin x\theta \sin (x + 1)\theta$

23. Find $\sum_0^{n-1} \sin^3 (a + bx)$.

24. Find $\sum_0^{n-1} \cos^3 (a + bx)$.

25. Find $\sum_0^{n-1} 2^x \tan 2^x\theta$.

26. Show that $\left[\sum_1^n \sin (2x - 1)\theta\right] \div \left[\sum_1^n \cos (2x - 1)\theta\right] = \tan n\theta$.

27. Find $\sum_1^n \cos^x \theta \cos x\theta$.

28. Find $\sum_1^n \cos x\theta \sec^x \theta$.

29. Show that $\left[\sum_1^n \sin x\theta\right] \div \left[\sum_1^n \cos x\theta\right] = \tan \dfrac{n + 1}{2} (\theta)$.

30. Find $\sum_0^{n-1} 2^x \sin \dfrac{\theta}{2^x} \left(\sin \dfrac{\theta}{2^{x+1}}\right)^2$.

31. Find $\sum_1^n \arctan \dfrac{1}{1 + x + x^2}$.

32. Find $\sum_1^n \dfrac{1}{2^x} \log \tan 2^x\theta$.

33. Find $\sum_1^n \sin \dfrac{\theta}{2^{x-1}} \sin \dfrac{3\theta}{2^{x-1}}$.

34. Find $\sum_1^n \dfrac{1}{\cos \theta + \cos (2x + 1)\theta}$.

35. Find $\sum_1^n \dfrac{\sin 2x\theta}{\cos (2x - 1)\theta \cos (2x + 1)\theta}$.

36. Find $\sum_1^n \tan \dfrac{\theta}{2^x} \sec 2\left(\dfrac{\theta}{2^x}\right)$.

37. Find $\sum_1^n \sec x\theta \sec (x + 1)\theta$.

4. STIRLING NUMBERS

It has been observed that the finite calculus makes much use of factorial expressions. The operations of reducing factorials to polynomials and vice versa are facilitated by Stirling's Numbers which we now discuss.

The factorial polynomial of degree n

$$x^{(n)} = x(x - 1)(x - 2) \cdots (x - n + 1) \tag{1}$$

we have noted, plays a role in the finite calculus similar to that played by x^n in the infinitesimal calculus. Since

$$x^{(n)} = x^{(m)}(x - m)^{(n-m)}, \quad m < n$$

it is convenient, in order that this equation hold for $m = 0$, to define $x^{(0)}$ to be 1. Evidently $x^{(n)}$ equals zero for $x = 0, 1, 2, \cdots, (n - 1)$, whereas if x is an integer greater than $(n - 1)$, we may write

$$x^{(n)} = \frac{x!}{(x - n)!}$$

If the multiplication on the right in (1) is performed a polynomial of degree n in x will result. Thus, $x^{(n)}$ may be written

$$x^{(n)} = S_1{}^n x + S_2{}^n x^2 + S_3{}^n x^3 + \cdots + S_n{}^n x^n = \sum_{i=1}^{n} S_i{}^n x^i \tag{2}$$

The upper index of $S_i{}^n$ is the degree of the polynomial under consideration and the lower index is that of the power of x with which it is associated. The numbers $S_i{}^n$ are called *Stirling Numbers of the First Kind*.

Thus

$$x^{(n)} = \sum_{i=1}^{n} S_i{}^n x^i \tag{2}$$

and

$$x^{(n+1)} = \sum_{i=1}^{n+1} S_i{}^{n+1} x^i$$

But

$$x^{(n+1)} = x^{(n)}(x - n)$$

and from (2)

$$x^{(n+1)} = x^{(n)}(x - n) = \sum_{i=1}^{n} S_i{}^n x^i (x - n)$$

Therefore

$$\sum_{i=1}^{n+1} S_i{}^{n+1} x^i = \sum_{i=1}^{n} S_i{}^n x^i (x - n)$$

By equating coefficients of x^i in the above equation, noting that

$$(S^n{}_{i-1} x^{i-1} + S_i{}^n x^i)(x - n)$$

contains two terms in x^i, we have the recurrence relation

$$S_i{}^{n+1} = S^n{}_{i-1} - n S_i{}^n \tag{3}$$

Also, by equating coefficients in (2) we note $S_0{}^n = 0$ and $S_n{}^n = 1$. Further, $S_i{}^n = 0$ if $i > n$.

Applying (3) we have, for examples,

$$S_1{}^2 = S_0{}^1 - S_1{}^1 = -1, \quad S_2{}^2 = S_1{}^1 - S_2{}^1 = 1 - 0 = 1$$

$$S_1{}^3 = S_0{}^2 - 2S_1{}^2 = 0 - 2(-1) = 2$$

$$S_2{}^3 = S_1{}^2 - 2S_2{}^2 = -1 - 2(1) = -3$$

A table of these numbers is easily constructed.

TABLE 6. TABLE OF STIRLING NUMBERS: FIRST KIND

$S_i{}^n$ \\ n	$S_1{}^n$	$S_2{}^n$	$S_3{}^n$	$S_4{}^n$	$S_5{}^n$	$S_6{}^n$	$S_7{}^n$
1	1						
2	−1	1					
3	2	−3	1				
4	−6	11	−6	1			
5	24	−50	35	−10	1		
6	−120	274	−225	85	−15	1	
7	720	−1764	1624	−735	175	−21	1

Using formula (3) any entry in the table is the number above and to the left minus the product of the number immediately above and the number n in that row. Thus

$$-225 = -50 - 5(35) = -50 - 175$$

$$274 = 24 - 5(-50) = 24 + 250$$

If we put $x = 1$ in (2) we obtain, $(n > 1)$,

$$S_1{}^n + S_2{}^n + S_3{}^n + \cdots + S_n{}^n = \sum_{i=1}^{n} S_i{}^n = 0 \qquad (4)$$

That is, the sum of the numbers in each row of the table to the right of the double vertical line is equal to zero. This fact can serve as a check in constructing the table.

With the table at hand we can immediately write down the polynomial that is equal to any factorial whose form is $x^{(n)}$. Thus,

$$x^{(6)} = x^6 - 15x^5 + 85x^4 - 225x^3 + 274x^2 - 120x$$

Stirling's Numbers of the First Kind also afford another method for expressing polynomials in terms of factorials. Again let us return to the problem of expressing

$$P_x = 2x^3 - 3x^2 + 3x - 10$$

in terms of factorials. By continued subtraction of factorial expressions we finally arrive at a zero remainder. Thus, detaching the coefficients,

$$P_x = 2 - 3 + 3 - 10$$
$$2x^{(3)} = 2 - 6 + 4$$

Diff. $= \qquad 3 - 1 - 10$
$$3x^{(2)} = \qquad 3 - 3$$

Diff. $= \qquad 2 - 10$
$$2x^{(1)} = \qquad 2$$

Diff. $= \qquad -10$
$$-10x^{(0)} = \qquad -10$$

Diff. $= \qquad 0$

We thus have

$$P_x - 2x^{(3)} - 3x^{(2)} - 2x^{(1)} + 10x^{(0)} = 0$$

$$P_x = 2x^{(3)} + 3x^{(2)} + 2x^{(1)} - 10$$

Exercises

1. Verify the numbers in Table 6 by expanding $x^{(2)}$, $x^{(3)}$, $\cdots$, $x^{(7)}$.
2. Find the values of $S_i{}^8$, $i = 1, 2, \cdots, 8$, by expanding Table 6 downward according to equation (3). Verify your result by expanding $x^{(8)}$.
3. Find the value of $x^{(7)} - 4x^{(6)} - 5x^{(5)}$.

It is fairly obvious that the expansion of the factorials in terms of the Stirling Numbers affords a method of differentiating and integrating factorial expressions and binomial coefficients. Thus, since

$$x^{(n)} = \sum_{i=1}^{n} S_i{}^n x^i$$

we have

$$Dx^{(n)} = \sum_{i=1}^{n} iS_i{}^n x^{i-1}$$

and

$$\int x^{(n)} \, dx = \sum_{i=1}^{n} \int S_i{}^n x^i \, dx + C$$

Similarly

$$\frac{x^{(n)}}{n!} = \binom{x}{n} = \frac{1}{n!} \sum_{i=1}^{n} S_i{}^n x^i$$

and hence

$$D\binom{x}{n} = \frac{1}{n!} \sum_{i=1}^{n} i S_i{}^n x^{i-1}$$

$$\int \binom{x}{n} dx = \frac{1}{n!} \int \sum_{i=1}^{n} S_i{}^n x^i \, dx + C$$

By means of the Maclaurin expansion

$$U_x = \sum_{i=0}^{n} x^i \left[\frac{D^i U_x}{i!} \right]_{x=0}$$

if $U_x = x^{(n)}$, we obtain

$$x^{(n)} = \sum_{i=0}^{n} x^i \left[\frac{D^i x^{(n)}}{i!} \right]_{x=0}$$

Comparing this expansion with (2) we have

$$S_i{}^n = \left[\frac{D^i x^{(n)}}{i!} \right]_{x=0}$$

and thus the Stirling Numbers of the First Kind are expressed in terms of the derivatives of factorial expressions. Thus

$$S_0{}^n = 0, \quad S_1{}^1 = Dx \Big]_{x=0} = 1, \quad S_1{}^2 = \frac{Dx^{(2)}}{1!} \Big]_{x=0} = -1$$

$$S_2{}^2 = \frac{D^2 x^{(2)}}{2!} \Big]_{x=0} = 1, \text{ etc.}$$

To derive by this procedure the recurrence relation (3) we shall need to apply Leibnitz's Theorem [3] for differentiating a product:

$$D^n uv = \sum_{i=0}^{n} \binom{n}{i} D^i u D^{n-i} v$$

Recalling that

$$x^{(n+1)} = (x - n)x^{(n)}$$

if, in the Leibnitz Theorem, we put $u = x - n$ and $v = x^{(n)}$, we obtain

$$D^i x^{(n+1)} = (x - n) D^i x^{(n)} + i D^{i-1} x^{(n)}$$

since all derivatives of $(x - n)$ after the first are equal to zero.

[3] Wilson, E. B., *Advanced Calculus*, p. 11. See Appendix I, this text, p. 135.

Dividing the above equation by $i!$ and setting $x = 0$, we obtain

$$\frac{D^i x^{(n+1)}}{i!}\bigg]_{x=0} = (x - n)\frac{D^i x^{(n)}}{i!}\bigg]_{x=0} + \frac{D^{i-1} x^{(n)}}{(i-1)!}\bigg]_{x=0}$$

which, by the Maclaurin expansion definition, may be written

$$S_i^{n+1} = -n S_i^n + S^n_{i-1}$$

which is our former equation (3).

In expanding factorial expressions into polynomials the coefficients of the powers of x were called Stirling Numbers of the First Kind. In a similar manner when we express powers of x in terms of factorials the coefficients of the factorial expressions are called Stirling Numbers of the Second Kind. For example, we may easily verify that

$$x = x^{(1)} = S_1{}^1 x^{(1)} \quad \text{and} \quad S_1{}^1 = 1$$

$$x^2 = x^{(1)} + x^{(2)} = S_1{}^2 x^{(1)} + S_2{}^2 x^{(2)} \quad \text{and} \quad S_1{}^2 = 1, \quad S_2{}^2 = 1$$

$$x^3 = x^{(1)} + 3x^{(2)} + x^{(3)} = S_1{}^3 x^{(1)} + S_2{}^3 x^{(2)} + S_3{}^3 x^{(3)}$$

$$\text{and} \quad S_1{}^3 = 1, \quad S_2{}^3 = 3, \quad S_3{}^3 = 1$$

wherein we indicate the Stirling Numbers of the Second Kind by $S_i{}^n$.

In a similar manner if

$$x^4 = S_1{}^4 x^{(1)} + S_2{}^4 x^{(2)} + S_3{}^4 x^{(3)} + S_4{}^4 x^{(4)}$$

$$x^5 = S_1{}^5 x^{(1)} + S_2{}^5 x^{(2)} + S_3{}^5 x^{(3)} + S_4{}^5 x^{(4)} + S_5{}^5 x^{(5)}$$

we find

$$S_1{}^4 = 1, \quad S_2{}^4 = 7, \quad S_3{}^4 = 6, \quad S_4{}^4 = 1$$

$$S_1{}^5 = 1, \quad S_2{}^5 = 15, \quad S_3{}^5 = 25, \quad S_4{}^5 = 10, \quad S_5{}^5 = 1$$

We adopt the symbol $S_i{}^n$ to represent these numbers. The upper index is that of the power of x under consideration, and the lower index is that of the factorial with which it is associated. In general, then, we have

$$x^n = S_1{}^n x^{(1)} + S_2{}^n x^{(2)} + S_3{}^n x^{(3)} + \cdots$$

$$+ S^n{}_{i-1} x^{(i-1)} + S_i{}^n x^{(i)} + \cdots + S_n{}^n x^{(n)} \quad (5)$$

or

$$x^n = \sum_{i=1}^{n} S_i{}^n x^{(i)} \quad (5)$$

From our definition we conclude immediately that $S_0{}^n = 0$, $S^n{}_{n+m} = 0$ if $m > 0$. Equating coefficients of x^n we obtain $S_n{}^n = 1$. Further, if in (5) we put $x = 1$, we obtain $S_1{}^n = 1$.

If in Newton's formula,

$$U_x = \sum_{i=0}^{n} x^{(i)} \frac{\Delta^i U_0}{i!} = \sum_{i=0}^{n} x^{(i)} \left[\frac{\Delta^i U_x}{i!}\right]_{x=0}$$

we put $U_x = x^n$ we obtain

$$x^n = x^{(1)}[\Delta x^n]_{x=0} + x^{(2)}\left[\frac{\Delta^2 x^n}{2!}\right]_{x=0} + \cdots + x^{(n)}\left[\frac{\Delta^n x^n}{n!}\right]_{x=0}$$

or

$$x^n = \sum_{i=1}^{n} x^{(i)} \left[\frac{\Delta^i x^n}{i!}\right]_{x=0}$$

In accordance with our definition we have

$$\mathcal{S}_i{}^n = \frac{\Delta^i x^n}{i!}\bigg]_{x=0} \tag{6}$$

We shall return to (6) later. Just now we seek a recurrence relation whereby the Stirling Numbers of any order can be found from those of lower order. To accomplish this we will need the simple relation

$$x^{(i+1)} + ix^{(i)} = x \cdot x^{(i)} \tag{7}$$

By definition

$$x^{n+1} = \mathcal{S}_1{}^{n+1}x^{(1)} + \mathcal{S}_2{}^{n+1}x^{(2)} + \cdots + \mathcal{S}_i{}^{n+1}x^{(i)} + \cdots + \mathcal{S}_{n+1}{}^{n+1}x^{(n+1)} \tag{8}$$

$$= \sum_{i=1}^{n+1} \mathcal{S}_i{}^{n+1}x^{(i)}$$

and from (5)

$$x^{n+1} = \mathcal{S}_1{}^n x x^{(1)} + \mathcal{S}_2{}^n x x^{(2)} + \cdots$$
$$+ \mathcal{S}^n{}_{i-1}x x^{(i-1)} + \mathcal{S}_i{}^n x x^{(i)} + \cdots + \mathcal{S}_n{}^n x x^{(n)} \tag{9}$$

or

$$x^{n+1} = \sum_{i=1}^{n} \mathcal{S}_i{}^n x x^{(i)} \tag{9}$$

Now the coefficient of $x^{(i)}$ in (8) is $\mathcal{S}_i{}^{n+1}$ and, employing (7), the coefficient of $x^{(i)}$ in (9) is $\mathcal{S}^n{}_{i-1} + i\mathcal{S}_i{}^n$.

Hence, equating these coefficients

$$\mathcal{S}_i{}^{n+1} = i\mathcal{S}_i{}^n + \mathcal{S}^n{}_{i-1} \tag{10}$$

For examples,

$$S_3{}^5 = 3S_3{}^4 + S_2{}^4 = 3(6) + 7 = 25$$

$$S_4{}^5 = 4S_4{}^4 + S_3{}^4 = 4(1) + 6 = 10$$

In Table 7, any entry by (10) is the number directly above multiplied by the value of i in the column plus the number above and to the left.

TABLE 7. TABLE OF STIRLING NUMBERS OF SECOND KIND: $S_i{}^n$

n \ $S_i{}^n$	$S_1{}^n$	$S_2{}^n$	$S_3{}^n$	$S_4{}^n$	$S_5{}^n$	$S_6{}^n$	$S_7{}^n$
1	1						
2	1	1					
3	1	3	1				
4	1	7	6	1			
5	1	15	25	10	1		
6	1	31	90	65	15	1	
7	1	63	301	350	140	21	1

Exercises

1. Extend Table 7 downward to find $S_i{}^8$, $i = 1, 2, \cdots, 8$.
2. Find DU_x if $U_x = x^{(8)} - 6x^{(7)} + x^{(5)}$.
3. Find $\int U_x \, dx$ if $U_x = x^{(8)} - 6x^{(7)} + x^{(5)}$.
4. In (5) let $x = -1$ and show that $(-1)^n = \sum_{i=1}^{n} (-1)^i S_i{}^n (i!)$.
5. Find $\Delta^i U_x$, $i = 1, 2, 3$, if $U_x = x^7 - 7x^6 + 8x^5 - 17x^3$.

Let us return to a consideration of equation (6)

$$S_i{}^n = \frac{\Delta^i x^n}{i!} \bigg]_{x=0}$$

which we may write

$$i! S_i{}^n = \Delta^i x^n]_{x=0}$$

The expression $\Delta^i x^n]_{x=0}$ is frequently written $\Delta^i 0^n$ so that

$$\Delta^i 0^n \equiv \Delta^i x^n]_{x=0}$$

The quantities $\Delta^i 0^n$ are known as "Differences of 0" because the leading term is always zero. We can form a table of these "Differences of 0" by multiplying the values of $S_i{}^n$ by $i!$.

TABLE 8. "DIFFERENCES OF 0," $\Delta^i 0^n = \Delta^i x^n]_{x=0}$

n	$x^n]_{x=0}$	$\Delta 0^n$	$\Delta^2 0^n$	$\Delta^3 0^n$	$\Delta^4 0^n$	$\Delta^5 0^n$
1	0^1	1				
2	0^2	1	2			
3	0^3	1	6	6		
4	0^4	1	14	36	24	
5	0^5	1	30	150	240	120

It is evident that the values in each row of Table 8 are the values of the function x^n, $n = 1, 2, 3, 4, 5$, and its leading differences when $x = 0$. That is, if $U_x = x^n$, the table gives U_0, ΔU_0, $\Delta^2 U_0$, etc.

By multiplying equation (10) by $i!$ we obtain

$$i! S_i^{n+1} = i! i S_i^n + i! S_{i-1}^n$$

or

$$\Delta^i 0^{n+1} = i[\Delta^i 0^n + \Delta^{i-1} 0^n] \tag{11}$$

since

$$i! S_{i-1}^n = i(i-1)! S_{i-1}^n = i \Delta^{i-1} 0^n$$

Applying this recurrence relation we have, for example,

$$\Delta^4 0^5 = 4[24 + 36] = 240$$

Interpreting the recurrence relation (11), we note that any entry in Table 8 is the sum of the number directly above and the number directly above and to the left, this sum multiplied by i, the index on the Δ, above.

Exercises

1. Show that $\Delta 0^n = 1$.

2. Show that $\Delta^m 0^n = m^n - m(m-1)^n + \dfrac{m^{(2)}}{2!}(m-2)^n + \cdots$.

3. Show that $\Delta^n 0^{n+1} = (n+1)! \dfrac{n}{2}$.

4. Show that $\Delta^n 0^n = n! = n^n - n(n-1)^n + \dfrac{n^{(2)}}{2!}(n-2)^n + \cdots$.

5. Show that $\Delta 0^n - \dfrac{\Delta^2 0^n}{2} + \dfrac{\Delta^3 0^n}{3} - \dfrac{\Delta^4 0^n}{4} + \cdots = 0$ if $n > 1$.

Chapter III*

BERNOULLI AND EULER POLYNOMIALS

---

1. BERNOULLI FUNCTIONS

In the study of polynomials we meet the problem: Find the polynomials of degree n in x, $P_n(x)$, such that

$$\Delta P_n(x) = \frac{x^{n-1}}{(n-1)!} \tag{1}$$

or

$$P_n(x) = \Delta^{-1} \frac{x^{n-1}}{(n-1)!} + C \tag{1'}$$

where we assume $P_n(x)$ to be of the form

$$P_n(x) = \sum_{i=0}^{n} A_i \frac{x^{n-i}}{(n-i)!} = A_0 \frac{x^n}{n!} + A_1 \frac{x^{n-1}}{(n-1)!} + \cdots + A_{n-1}x + A_n \tag{2}$$

From (1) we have

$$P_n(x+1) - P_n(x) = \frac{x^{n-1}}{(n-1)!}$$

which, upon differentiating with respect to x, becomes

$$P_n'(x+1) - P_n'(x) = \frac{x^{n-2}}{(n-2)!} \tag{3}$$

or

$$\Delta P_n'(x) = \frac{x^{n-2}}{(n-2)!} \tag{3}$$

Since from (1)

$$\Delta P_{n-1}(x) = \frac{x^{n-2}}{(n-2)!}$$

* This chapter may be omitted without destroying the continuity of the subject.

44

we have
$$\Delta P_n{}'(x) = \Delta P_{n-1}(x)$$

Hence,
$$P_n{}'(x) - P_{n-1}(x) = k \tag{4}$$

Since from (2) $P_n{}'(0) = A_{n-1}$, and $P_{n-1}(0) = A_{n-1}$, $k = 0$, and

$$P_n{}'(x) = P_{n-1}(x) \quad \text{or} \quad DP_n(x) = P_{n-1}(x) \tag{5}$$

Equations (1) and (5) thus completely define $P_n(x)$, the Bernoulli functions.

From (5)
$$P_2{}'(x) = A_0 x + A_1 = P_1(x)$$

and from (1) and (1'), respectively,

$$\Delta P_1(x) = 1 \quad \text{and} \quad P_1(x) = x + C_1$$

so that $A_0 = 1$. Further, using $A_0 = 1$ with (5),

$$P_3{}'(x) = \frac{x^2}{2!} + A_1 x + A_2 = P_2(x)$$

and from (1)

$$\Delta P_2(x) = x \quad \text{and} \quad P_2(x) = \frac{x^{(2)}}{2!} + C_2 = \frac{x^2}{2} - \frac{x}{2} + C_2$$

so that $A_1 = -\frac{1}{2}$.

Continuing this scheme we can find A_2, A_3, etc., but we will establish a more general method by deriving a recurrence relation among the A's.

We have from (2)

$$\Delta P_n(x) = \frac{A_0}{n!} \Delta x^n + \frac{A_1}{(n-1)!} \Delta x^{n-1} + \frac{A_2}{(n-2)!} \Delta x^{n-2}$$

$$+ \cdots + A_{n-1} \Delta x$$

$$\Delta P_n(x)]_{x=0} = \left[\sum_{i=0}^{n-1} \frac{A_i}{(n-i)!} \Delta x^{n-i} \right]_{x=0}$$

$$= \left[\sum_{i=0}^{n-1} \frac{A_i}{(n-i)!} [(x+1)^{n-i} - x^{n-i}] \right]_{x=0}$$

$$\Delta P_n(0) = \sum_{i=0}^{n-1} \frac{A_i}{(n-i)!}$$

From (1) if $n > 1$,
$$\Delta P_n(0) = 0$$

Therefore, for $n > 1$, we have

$$\sum_{i=0}^{n-1} \frac{A_i}{(n-i)!} \equiv \frac{A_0}{n!} + \frac{A_1}{(n-1)!} + \frac{A_2}{(n-2)!} + \cdots + A_{n-1} = 0 \quad (6)$$

$$n = 3: \qquad \frac{A_0}{3!} + \frac{A_1}{2!} + \frac{A_2}{1!} = 0, \quad A_2 = \frac{1}{12}$$

$$n = 4: \quad \frac{A_0}{4!} + \frac{A_1}{3!} + \frac{A_2}{2!} + \frac{A_3}{1!} = 0, \quad A_3 = 0$$

Continuing in this manner we find

$$A_4 = -\frac{1}{720}, \quad A_5 = 0, \quad A_6 = \frac{1}{30,240}, \quad A_7 = 0, \quad A_8 = \frac{-1}{1,209,600}$$

and so on.

We thus find the Bernoulli functions

$$P_1(x) = x - \tfrac{1}{2}$$

$$P_2(x) = \frac{x^2}{2} - \frac{x}{2} + \frac{1}{12}$$

$$P_3(x) = \frac{x^3}{6} - \frac{x^2}{4} + \frac{x}{12}$$

$$P_4(x) = \frac{x^4}{24} - \frac{x^3}{12} + \frac{x^2}{24} - \frac{1}{720}$$

$$P_5(x) = \frac{x^5}{120} - \frac{x^4}{48} + \frac{x^3}{72} - \frac{x}{720}$$

$$P_6(x) = \frac{x^6}{720} - \frac{x^5}{240} + \frac{x^4}{288} - \frac{x^2}{1440} + \frac{1}{30,240}$$

and so on.

2. Properties of the Polynomials, $P_n(x)$

Since

$$DP_n(x) = P_{n-1}(x) \quad (7)$$

it follows that

$$\int_a^b P_n(x)\,dx = P_{n+1}(b) - P_{n+1}(a), \quad n > 0 \quad (8)$$

In particular, since $P_n(0) = A_n$, and

$$P_n(1) = \sum_{0}^{n-1} \frac{A_i}{(n-i)!} + A_n = A_n$$

$$\int_0^1 P_n(x)\, dx = P_{n+1}(1) - P_{n+1}(0) = A_{n+1} - A_{n+1} = 0 \qquad (9)$$

We have seen that $A_1 = -\frac{1}{2}$ but that $A_3 = A_5 = A_7 = 0$.
We shall now show that $A_{2k-1} = 0$ for $k > 1$.
By definition,

$$\Delta P_{2k+1}(x) = \frac{x^{2k}}{(2k)!} \qquad (10)$$

or

$$P_{2k+1}(x+1) - P_{2k+1}(x) = \frac{x^{2k}}{(2k)!} \qquad (10')$$

In (10'), replacing x by $-x$, we obtain

$$P_{2k+1}(1-x) - P_{2k+1}(-x) = \frac{x^{2k}}{(2k)!} \qquad (11)$$

Let

$$F(x) = -P_{2k+1}(1-x) \qquad (12)$$

then

$$-P_{2k+1}(-x) = -P_{2k+1}[1-(x+1)] = F(x+1) \qquad (13)$$

and (11) becomes

$$F(x+1) - F(x) = \Delta F(x) = \frac{x^{2k}}{(2k)!} \qquad (14)$$

From (10) and (14) we have

$$\Delta F(x) = \Delta P_{2k+1}(x)$$

and hence

$$F(x) - P_{2k+1}(x) = C$$

from which

$$F'(x) - P'_{2k+1}(x) = 0 \qquad (15)$$

Using (12), equation (15) becomes

$$P'_{2k+1}(1-x) - P'_{2k+1}(x) = 0 \qquad (16)$$

Now recalling that

$$P_n'(x) = P_{n-1}(x)$$

equation (16) becomes

$$P_{2k}(1-x) = P_{2k}(x) \qquad (17)$$

Differentiating (17) we have for $k > 1$

$$-P'_{2k}(1 - x) = P'_{2k}(x)$$

$$-P_{2k-1}(1 - x) = P_{2k-1}(x), \quad k > 1$$

$$P_{2k-1}(x) + P_{2k-1}(1 - x) = 0$$

$$P_{2k-1}(0) + P_{2k-1}(1) = 0$$

$$A_{2k-1} + A_{2k-1} = 0$$

Hence

$$A_{2k-1} = 0 \quad \text{for } k > 1$$

3. BERNOULLI POLYNOMIALS AND NUMBERS

If the Bernoulli functions, $P_i(x)$, $i = 1, 2, \cdots, n$, are each multiplied by $i!$ we have the Bernoulli polynomials,[1] $B_i(x)$. That is,

$$B_n(x) = n!P_n(x) \tag{18}$$

Thus we have

$$B_0(x) = 1$$

$$B_1(x) = x - \tfrac{1}{2}$$

$$B_2(x) = x^2 - x + \tfrac{1}{6}$$

$$B_3(x) = x^3 - \tfrac{3}{2}x^2 + \frac{x}{2}$$

$$B_4(x) = x^4 - 2x^3 + x^2 - \tfrac{1}{30}$$

$$B_5(x) = x^5 - \tfrac{5}{2}x^4 + \tfrac{5}{3}x^3 - \frac{x}{6}$$

$$B_6(x) = x^6 - 3x^5 + \tfrac{5}{2}x^4 - \frac{x^2}{2} + \tfrac{1}{42}$$

$$B_7(x) = x^7 - \tfrac{7}{2}x^6 + \tfrac{7}{2}x^5 - \tfrac{7}{6}x^3 + \frac{x}{6}$$

$$B_8(x) = x^8 - 4x^7 + \tfrac{14}{3}x^6 - \tfrac{7}{3}x^4 + \tfrac{2}{3}x^2 - \tfrac{1}{30}$$

$$B_9(x) = x^9 - \tfrac{9}{2}x^8 + 6x^7 - \tfrac{21}{5}x^6 + 2x^3 - \tfrac{3}{10}x$$

$$B_{10}(x) = x^{10} - 5x^9 + \tfrac{15}{2}x^8 - 7x^6 + 5x^4 - \tfrac{3}{2}x^2 + \tfrac{5}{66}$$

[1] Authors are not in agreement in notation with regard to Bernoulli polynomials and numbers. Our notation is that of Nörlund, *Differenzenrechnung*, p. 18, and Steffensen, *Interpolation*, p. 120. Charles Jordan, *Finite Differences*, p. 230, calls our $P_n(x)$ Bernoulli polynomials.

The values of $B_n(x)$ for $x = 0$ are called Bernoulli's numbers and are denoted by B_n. That is, $B_n \equiv B_n(0)$. Thus we have

$$B_0 = 1 \qquad B_3 = 0 \qquad B_6 = \tfrac{1}{42} \qquad B_9 = 0$$

$$B_1 = -\tfrac{1}{2} \qquad B_4 = -\tfrac{1}{30} \qquad B_7 = 0 \qquad B_{10} = \tfrac{5}{66}$$

$$B_2 = \tfrac{1}{6} \qquad B_5 = 0 \qquad B_8 = -\tfrac{1}{30} \qquad B_{11} = 0$$

The Bernoulli polynomials, $B_n(x)$, enjoy many properties that are analogous to those of the functions, $P_n(x)$. To establish these properties generally all that is necessary is to employ our definition $B_n(x) = n!P_n(x)$, with the properties of $P_n(x)$. Thus

$$B_n'(x) = nB_{n-1}(x), \quad n \geq 1. \tag{19}$$

$$\int_a^b B_n(x)\, dx = \frac{1}{n+1}[B_{n+1}(b) - B_{n+1}(a)] \tag{20}$$

$$\int_0^1 B_n(x)\, dx = 0 \tag{20'}$$

Since $B_i = i!A_i$ we can write

$$P_n(x) = B_0 \frac{x^n}{n!} + B_1 \frac{x^{n-1}}{(n-1)!} + \frac{B_2}{2!}\frac{x^{n-2}}{(n-2)!} + \cdots + \frac{B_n}{n!} \tag{21}$$

$$= \frac{1}{n!}\sum_{i=0}^n \binom{n}{i} B_i x^{n-i} \tag{22}$$

which can also be written symbolically

$$P_n(x) = \frac{1}{n!}(x + B)^n \tag{23}$$

if B^i is replaced by B_i after the expansion.

Since

$$\Delta P_n(0) = 0, \quad n > 1$$

it follows from (23) that symbolically

$$(1 + B)^n - B^n = 0, \quad n > 1 \tag{24}$$

which reduces to

$$\sum_{i=0}^{n-1} \binom{n}{i} B_i = 0 \tag{25}$$

If (24) is expanded and B^i is replaced by $B_i = i!A_i$, the result divided by $n!$, the equation becomes

$$\sum_{i=0}^{n-1} \frac{A_i}{(n-i)!} = 0$$

which we have previously established.

Employing (24) we have

$$n = 2: \qquad\qquad 1 + 2B_1 = 0, \quad B_1 = -\tfrac{1}{2}$$

$$n = 3: \qquad\qquad 1 + 3B_1 + 3B_2 = 0, \quad B_2 = \tfrac{1}{6}$$

$$n = 4: \quad 1 + 4B_1 + 6B_2 + 4B_3 = 0, \quad B_3 = 0$$

and so on.

It has doubtless been noted that the absolute values of A_i decrease rapidly with increasing i whereas the absolute values of B_i after B_6 increase rapidly with i.

From

$$\Delta P_n(x) = \frac{x^{n-1}}{(n-1)!}$$

we get

$$\Delta n! P_n(x) = n x^{n-1}$$

or

$$\Delta B_n(x) = n x^{n-1} \qquad\qquad (26)$$

We can express (26) in the form

$$\Delta^{-1} x^n = \frac{B_{n+1}(x)}{n+1} + k$$

from which we obtain

$$\sum_{x=1}^{x-1} x^n = \Delta^{-1} x^n \Big]_{x=1}^{x} = \frac{B_{n+1}(x) - B_{n+1}(1)}{n+1}$$

Thus if $n = 2$ and $n = 3$ we have

$$\sum_{1}^{x-1} x^2 = 1^2 + 2^2 + \cdots + (x-1)^2 = \frac{B_3(x) - B_3(1)}{3}$$

$$= \frac{1}{3}\left[x^3 - \frac{3}{2}x^2 + \frac{x}{2}\right] = \frac{x(x-1)(2x-1)}{6}$$

$$\sum_{1}^{x-1} x^3 = 1^3 + 2^3 + \cdots + (x-1)^3 = \frac{B_4(x) - B_4(1)}{4}$$

$$= \frac{1}{4}\left\{\left[x^4 - 2x^3 + x^2 - \frac{1}{30}\right] - \left[-\frac{1}{30}\right]\right\} = \left[\frac{x(x-1)}{2}\right]^2$$

4. Other Developments of the Bernoulli Functions

The Bernoulli functions, polynomials, and numbers may be developed by other processes. Books on advanced calculus, infinite series, etc., devote considerable emphasis to these developments and their applications.[2] For example, the Bernoulli numbers, for x sufficiently small, may be defined by the expansion

$$\frac{x}{e^x - 1} = B_0 + B_1 x + \frac{B_2 x^2}{2!} + \frac{B_3 x^3}{3!} + \cdots \tag{27}$$

which may be written,

$$\left(1 + \frac{x}{2!} + \frac{x^2}{3!} - \cdots\right)\left(B_0 + B_1 x + B_2 \frac{x^2}{2!} + \cdots\right) = 1$$

Then the equations for determining B_n are

$$B_0 = 1$$

$$\frac{1}{2!}\frac{B_0}{0!} + \frac{1}{1!}\frac{B_1}{1!} = 0$$

$$\frac{1}{3!}\frac{B_0}{0!} + \frac{1}{2!}\frac{B_1}{1!} + \frac{1}{1!}\frac{B_2}{2!} = 0$$

. . . .

$$\frac{1}{n!}\frac{B_0}{0!} + \frac{1}{(n-1)!}\frac{B_1}{1!} + \frac{1}{(n-2)!}\frac{B_2}{2!} + \cdots + \frac{1}{1!}\frac{B_{n-1}}{(n-1)!} = 0 \tag{28}$$

If we multiply the above equation by $n!$ it can be written

$$\binom{n}{0} B_0 + \binom{n}{1} B_1 + \binom{n}{2} B_2 + \cdots + \binom{n}{n-1} B_{n-1} = 0$$

or symbolically

$$(1 + B)^n - B^n = 0 \tag{29}$$

Writing (27) in the form

$$\frac{x}{e^x - 1} = 1 - \frac{x}{2} + \frac{B_2 x^2}{2!} + \frac{B_3 x^3}{3!} + \cdots \tag{30}$$

we obtain

$$\frac{x}{e^x - 1} + \frac{x}{2} = 1 + \frac{B_2 x^2}{2!} + \cdots$$

[2] Wilson, E. B., *Advanced Calculus*, pp. 448–451; Sokolnikoff, I. S., *Advanced Calculus*, p. 286; Knopp, K., *Theorie und Anwendung der Unendlichen Reihen*, p. 175.

The left-hand member is, however,

$$= \frac{x}{2}\left(\frac{2}{e^x - 1} + 1\right) = \frac{x}{2}\left(\frac{e^x + 1}{e^x - 1}\right)$$

$$= \frac{x}{2}\frac{e^{\frac{x}{2}} + e^{-\frac{x}{2}}}{e^{\frac{x}{2}} - e^{-\frac{x}{2}}} = \frac{x}{2}\coth\frac{x}{2} \tag{31}$$

which we recognize to be an even function of x, and consequently all the B's with odd subscripts, except B_1, are zero. Incidentally we have shown that

$$\frac{x}{2}\coth\frac{x}{2} = 1 + \frac{B_2 x^2}{2!} + \frac{B_4 x^4}{4!} - \cdots$$

from which we obtain immediately

$$\coth x = \frac{1}{x} + \frac{x}{3} - \frac{x^3}{45} + \frac{2x^5}{945} - \cdots + \frac{B_{2n}(2x)^{2n}}{(2n)!x} - \cdots$$

Replacing in (31) $x/2$ by z we obtain

$$z\frac{e^z + e^{-z}}{e^z - e^{-z}} = 1 + \frac{B_2}{2!}(2z)^2 + \frac{B_4}{4!}(2z)^4 - \cdots \tag{32}$$

If now in (32) we replace z by it we get

$$t\cot t = 1 - 2^2\frac{B_2 t^2}{2!} + 2^4\frac{B_4}{4!}t^4 - \cdots + (-1)^n\frac{2^{2n}B_{2n}t^{2n}}{(2n)!} - \cdots$$

$$= 1 - \tfrac{1}{3}t^2 - \tfrac{1}{45}t^4 - \tfrac{2}{945}t^6 - \tfrac{1}{4725}t^8 - \cdots$$

Recalling that

$$2\cot 2t = \cot t - \tan t$$

or

$$\tan t = \cot t - 2\cot 2t$$

we obtain

$$\tan t = \sum_{n=1}^{\infty}\frac{(-1)^{n-1}2^{2n}(2^{2n} - 1)B_{2n}}{(2n)!}t^{2n-1}$$

$$= t + \tfrac{1}{3}t^3 + \tfrac{2}{15}t^5 + \tfrac{17}{315}t^7 - \cdots$$

With the aid of the identity

$$\cot x + \tan\frac{x}{2} = \frac{1}{\sin x}$$

employing the two preceding expansions we obtain

$$\frac{t}{\sin t} = t \csc t = \sum_{n=0}^{\infty} \frac{(-1)^{n-1}(2^{2n} - 2)B_{2n}}{(2n)!} t^{2n}$$

$$= 1 + \frac{t^2}{6} + \frac{7}{360} t^4 + \frac{31}{15,120} t^6 + \cdots$$

By integrating both members of $\tan t$ given above we obtain

$$\log \cos t = -\frac{t^2}{2} - \frac{t^4}{12} - \frac{t^6}{45} - \cdots$$

$$- (-1)^{n-1}(2^{2n} - 1)2^{2n}B_{2n} \frac{t^{2n}}{2n(2n)!} - \cdots$$

The Bernoulli polynomials may be defined by the expansion

$$\frac{te^{tx}}{e^t - 1} = B_0(x) + B_1(x)t + B_2(x)\frac{t^2}{2!} + B_3(x)\frac{t^3}{3!} + \cdots \tag{33}$$

Multiplying both members by $e^t - 1$ we obtain

$$t\left(1 + tx + \frac{t^2x^2}{2!} + \frac{t^3x^3}{3!} + \cdots\right)$$

$$= \left(t + \frac{t^2}{2!} + \frac{t^3}{3!} + \frac{t^4}{4!} + \cdots\right)\left(B_0(x) + B_1(x)t + B_2(x)\frac{t^2}{2!} + \cdots\right)$$

Equating coefficients of t we obtain

$$B_0(x) = 1$$
$$B_1(x) = x - \tfrac{1}{2}$$
$$B_2(x) = x^2 - x + \tfrac{1}{6}$$
$$B_3(x) = x^3 - \tfrac{3}{2}x^2 + \tfrac{1}{2}x$$
$$B_4(x) = x^4 - 2x^3 + x^2 - \tfrac{1}{30}$$

and so on.

Differentiating (33) with respect to x and dividing by t we obtain the relation

$$B_n'(x) = nB_{n-1}(x) \tag{33'}$$

Of course from (33')

$$\int_a^x B_n(x) \, dx = \frac{1}{n+1} [B_{n+1}(x) - B_{n+1}(a)]$$

Equation (33) may be written

$$\frac{te^{tx}}{e^t - 1} = \sum_{n=0}^{\infty} B_n(x) \frac{t^n}{n!} \tag{33}$$

In this equation replace x by $(1 - x)$. Then

$$\frac{te^{t(1-x)}}{e^t - 1} = \sum_{n=0}^{\infty} B_n(1 - x) \frac{t^n}{n!} \tag{34}$$

But

$$\frac{te^{-tx} \cdot e^t}{e^t - 1} = \frac{te^{-tx}}{1 - e^{-t}} = \frac{-te^{-tx}}{e^{-t} - 1} = \sum_{n=0}^{\infty} B_n(x) \frac{(-t)^n}{n!} \tag{34'}$$

Equating coefficients of t^n in (34') and (34) we obtain

$$B_n(1 - x) = (-1)^n B_n(x) \tag{35}$$

If $n = 2k$, (35) becomes

$$B_{2k}(1 - x) = B_{2k}(x) \tag{36}$$

Exercises

1. Show that $\dfrac{P_n(x) + P_{n+1}(x)}{2} = P_n(x) + \dfrac{x^{n-1}}{2(n-1)!}$.

2. Show that $\displaystyle\int_z^{z+1} P_n(x)\, dx = \Delta P_{n+1}(z) = \dfrac{z^n}{n!}$.

3. Show that $B_{n+1}(x)$ satisfies the difference equation $U_{x+1} - U_x = (n + 1)x^n$.

4. Obtain the developments:

   (a) $\log \sin x = \log x - \dfrac{x^2}{6} - \dfrac{x^4}{180} - \dfrac{x^6}{2835} - \cdots - \dfrac{(-1)^n B_{2n}(2x)^{2n}}{2n(2n)!} - \cdots$.

   (b) $\log \sinh x = \log x + \dfrac{x^2}{6} - \dfrac{x^4}{180} + \dfrac{x^6}{2835} - \cdots + \dfrac{B_{2n}(2x)^{2n}}{2n(2n)!} - \cdots$.

5. From the identity $\dfrac{1}{e^x - 1} - \dfrac{2}{e^{2x} - 1} = \dfrac{1}{e^x + 1}$ derive the expansions:

   (a) $\dfrac{1}{e^x + 1} = \dfrac{1}{2} - B_2(2^2 - 1)\dfrac{x}{2!} - B_4(2^4 - 1)\dfrac{x^3}{4!} - \cdots - B_{2n}(2^{2n} - 1)\dfrac{x^{2n-1}}{(2n)!} - \cdots$.

   (b) $\dfrac{e^x}{e^x + 1} = \dfrac{1}{2} + B_2(2^2 - 1)\dfrac{x}{2!} + B_4(2^4 - 1)\dfrac{x^3}{4!} + \cdots + B_{2n}(2^{2n} - 1)\dfrac{x^{2n-1}}{(2n)!} - \cdots$.

6. Show that the values of A_i, $i = 0, 1, 2, \cdots, n$, can be found from

   $$\frac{t}{-1} = \sum_{i=0}^{\infty} A_i t^i.$$

5. Bernoulli Polynomials of the Second Kind

We have found that the Bernoulli functions $P_n(x)$ are completely defined by the formulas

$$\text{(a)} \quad \Delta P_n(x) = \frac{x^{n-1}}{(n-1)!} \quad \text{and} \quad \text{(b)} \quad DP_n(x) = P_{n-1}(x)$$

To distinguish these functions, $P_n(x)$, and $B_n(x)$ which were immediately derived from them, from new functions we are about to discuss we call the above functions, polynomials, and numbers the Bernoulli functions, polynomials, and numbers of the *first kind*.

Let $p_n(x)$ denote a polynomial of degree n which has the property

$$Dp_n(x) = \frac{x^{(n-1)}}{(n-1)!} = \binom{x}{n-1} \tag{37}$$

By integration

$$p_n(x) = \int \frac{x^{(n-1)}}{(n-1)!} \, dx + k$$

which shows that $p_n(x)$ is not completely defined by (37).

Let $p_n(x)$ be written in the factorial form

$$p_n(x) = b_0 \frac{x^{(n)}}{n!} + b_1 \frac{x^{(n-1)}}{(n-1)!} + \cdots + b_{n-1}x + b_n \tag{38}$$

From (37) we have

$$Dp_{n-1}(x) = \Delta Dp_n(x) = \frac{x^{(n-2)}}{(n-2)!}$$

Hence

$$\Delta Dp_n(x) = Dp_{n-1}(x) \tag{39}$$

Integrating (39) we have

$$\Delta p_n(x) = p_{n-1}(x) + C$$

Let $x = 0$. Then from (38)

$$\Delta p_n(0) = p_{n-1}(0) = b_{n-1}$$

and hence $C = 0$. We then have

$$\Delta p_n(x) = p_{n-1}(x) \tag{40}$$

Thus, equations (37) and (40) completely determine $p_n(x)$ which is called a Bernoulli polynomial of the *second* kind.

From (37), $Dp_1(x) = 1$ and hence $p_1(x) = x + k$. Therefore $b_0 = 1$.

Again from (37)

$$p_2(x) = \frac{x^2}{2} + k = \frac{x^{(2)}}{2} + \frac{x}{2} + k$$

and from (38)

$$p_2(x) = b_0 \frac{x^{(2)}}{2} + b_1 x + b_2$$

hence $b_1 = \frac{1}{2}$.

By this same procedure we can find $b_2 = -\frac{1}{12}$, $b_3 = \frac{1}{24}$, and so on. A better procedure is to find a recurrence relation among the b's. From (37) $Dp_n(0) = 0$ if $n > 1$, and from (38)

$$Dp_n(x)]_{x=0} = \frac{b_0}{n!} Dx^{(n)}\bigg]_{x=0} + \frac{b_1}{(n-1)!} Dx^{(n-1)}\bigg]_{x=0} + \cdots + b_{n-1}Dx]_{x=0}$$

$$(41)$$

But

$$Dx^{(n)}]_{x=0} = S_1{}^n \quad \text{and} \quad S_1{}^n = -(n-1)S_1{}^{n-1} = (-1)^{n-1}(n-1)!S_1{}^1$$

Hence, recalling that $S_1{}^1 = 1$, we have

$$\frac{1}{n!} Dx^{(n)}\bigg]_{x=0} = \frac{(-1)^{n-1}}{n}$$

Therefore, substituting in (41) we have

$$\frac{1}{n} - \frac{b_1}{n-1} + \frac{b_2}{n-2} - \cdots + (-1)^{n-1}b_{n-1} = 0 \qquad (42)$$

Giving n the values 2, 3, 4, $\cdots$ successively we obtain

$$\frac{1}{2} - b_1 = 0 \qquad\qquad b_1 = \frac{1}{2}$$

$$\frac{1}{3} - \frac{b_1}{2} + b_2 = 0 \qquad\qquad b_2 = -\frac{1}{12}$$

$$\frac{1}{4} - \frac{b_1}{3} + \frac{b_2}{2} - b_3 = 0 \qquad\qquad b_3 = \frac{1}{24}$$

and so on.

Other values of b_i are

$$b_4 = -\frac{19}{720} \qquad\qquad\qquad b_7 = \frac{275}{24,192}$$

$$b_5 = \frac{3}{160} \qquad\qquad\qquad b_8 = -\frac{33,953}{3,628,800}$$

$$b_6 = -\frac{863}{60,480}$$

Hence we have

$$p_1(x) = x + \tfrac{1}{2}$$

$$p_2(x) = \frac{x^{(2)}}{2!} + \frac{1}{2}x - \frac{1}{12}$$

$$p_3(x) = \frac{x^{(3)}}{3!} + \frac{1}{2}\frac{x^{(2)}}{2!} - \frac{1}{12}x + \frac{1}{24}$$

$$p_4(x) = \frac{x^{(4)}}{4!} + \frac{1}{2}\frac{x^{(3)}}{3!} - \frac{1}{12}\frac{x^{(2)}}{2!} + \frac{1}{24}x - \frac{19}{720}$$

$$p_5(x) = \frac{x^{(5)}}{5!} + \frac{1}{2}\frac{x^{(4)}}{4!} - \frac{1}{12}\frac{x^{(3)}}{3!} + \frac{1}{24}\frac{x^{(2)}}{2!} - \frac{19}{720}x + \frac{3}{160}$$

and so on.

From (38) we note that

$$p_n(0) = b_n$$

$$p_n(1) = b_{n-1} + b_n$$

and thus it follows that

$$\int_0^1 \frac{x^{(n)}}{n!}\,dx = p_{n+1}(1) - p_{n+1}(0) = b_n + b_{n+1} - b_{n+1} = b_n \qquad (43)$$

Since

$$Dp_{n+1}(x) = \frac{x^{(n)}}{n!} = \frac{1}{n!}[S_1{}^n x + S_2{}^n x^2 + \cdots + S_n{}^n x^n] = \frac{1}{n!}\sum_{i=1}^n S_i{}^n x^i$$

$$p_{n+1}(x) = \frac{1}{n!}\sum_{i=1}^n S_i{}^n \frac{x^{i+1}}{i+1} + k$$

But

$$p_{n+1}(0) = b_{n+1}$$

Hence $k = b_{n+1}$ and

$$p_{n+1}(x) = \frac{1}{n!}\sum_{i=1}^n S_i{}^n \frac{x^{i+1}}{i+1} + b_{n+1} \qquad (44)$$

which expresses the Bernoulli polynomial of the second kind as a power series.

In (44) let $x = 1$. We obtain

$$p_{n+1}(1) = b_n + b_{n+1} = \frac{1}{n!}\sum_{i=1}^n S_i{}^n \frac{1}{i+1} + b_{n+1}$$

and

$$b_n = \frac{1}{n!} \sum_{i=1}^{n} S_i{}^n \frac{1}{i+1} \qquad (45)$$

Consequently, with the aid of the Stirling Numbers of the First Kind we can obtain the coefficients b_i. For example,

$$b_4 = \frac{1}{4!}\left[S_1{}^4 \cdot \frac{1}{2} + S_2{}^4 \cdot \frac{1}{3} + S_3{}^4 \cdot \frac{1}{4} + S_4{}^4 \cdot \frac{1}{5} \right]$$

$$= \frac{1}{4!}\left[-\frac{6}{2} + \frac{11}{3} - \frac{6}{4} + \frac{1}{5} \right] = -\frac{19}{720}$$

We have observed that the values of A_i diminish rapidly in absolute value with increasing i, although we have no technique for finding the limiting value of A_i as i becomes infinite. However, we can establish that b_n approaches zero in absolute value as n becomes infinite.

To establish this we return to (43)

$$b_n = \int_0^1 \frac{x^{(n)}}{n!}\, dx$$

and write

$$\frac{x^{(n)}}{n!} = x \cdot \frac{x-1}{1} \cdot \frac{x-2}{2} \cdot \ldots \cdot \frac{x-n+1}{n-1} \cdot \frac{1}{n}$$

in which the absolute value of each factor is less than 1 for $0 < x < 1$. Hence,

$$\left| \frac{x^{(n)}}{n!} \right| < \frac{1}{n}, \quad \text{and} \quad \lim_{n \to \infty} |b_n| = 0$$

6. EULER POLYNOMIALS

The Euler polynomial of degree n in x, $E_n(x)$, is defined by the equation

$$\frac{1}{2}[E_n(x+1) + E_n(x)] = \frac{x^n}{n!} \qquad (46)$$

where

$$E_n(x) = e_0 \frac{x^n}{n!} + e_1 \frac{x^{n-1}}{(n-1)!} + \cdots + e_{n-1}x + e_n \qquad (47)$$

We have

$$E_{n-1}(x) = e_0 \frac{x^{n-1}}{(n-1)!} + e_1 \frac{x^{n-2}}{(n-2)!} + \cdots + e_{n-1}$$

hence

$$DE_n(x) = E_{n-1}(x) \qquad (48)$$

The equations (46) and (48) completely define $E_n(x)$.

If in (46) we assign n the value 0 we have

$$\tfrac{1}{2}[E_0(x+1) + E_0(x)] = 1$$

which is satisfied when $E_0(x) = 1$ and hence from (47) $e_0 = 1$. We can arrive at this conclusion in another manner: In (47) find $E_n(x+1)$ and add to $E_n(x)$, then divide their sum by 2 and equate to $x^n/n!$ in accordance with (46). Equating coefficients of $x^n/n!$ we find $e_0 = 1$. Since from (47) $E_0(x) = e_0$, we have $E_0(x) = 1$.

Again, following the steps outlined in the preceding paragraph we find

$$\left.\frac{E_n(x+1) + E_n(x)}{2}\right]_{x=0} = \frac{1}{2}\left[\frac{e_0}{n!} + \frac{e_1}{(n-1)!} + \cdots + \frac{e_{n-1}}{1!}\right] + e_n$$

$$= \frac{1}{2}\sum_{i=0}^{n-1}\frac{e_i}{(n-i)!} + e_n = 0 \qquad (49)$$

This conclusion is enhanced by noting that

$$\tfrac{1}{2}[(x+1)^i - x^i]_{x=0} = \tfrac{1}{2}, \quad i > 0$$

It may also be noted from (46) that

$$\tfrac{1}{2}[E_n(1) + E_n(0)] = 0 \qquad (50)$$

Returning to (49) we can compute the remaining coefficients e_i, $i = 1, 2, 3, \cdots, n$. We have, starting with $e_0 = 1$,

$$n = 1: \qquad \frac{1}{2}\frac{1}{1!} + e_1 = 0 \quad \text{which gives } e_1 = -\tfrac{1}{2}$$

$$n = 2: \qquad \frac{1}{2}\left[\frac{1}{2!} + \frac{e_1}{1!}\right] + e_2 = 0 \quad \text{which gives } e_2 = 0$$

$$n = 3: \qquad \frac{1}{2}\left[\frac{1}{3!} + \frac{e_1}{2!} + \frac{e_2}{1!}\right] + e_3 = 0 \quad \text{which gives } e_3 = \tfrac{1}{24}$$

Continuing this procedure we find

$$e_{2n} = 0, \quad n > 0$$

$$e_5 = -\frac{1}{240}, \quad e_7 = \frac{17}{40,320}, \quad e_9 = -\frac{31}{725,760}$$

and so on.

The Euler polynomials are then immediate:

$$E_0(x) = 1, \quad E_1(x) = x - \tfrac{1}{2}, \quad E_2(x) = \frac{x^2}{2} - \frac{x}{2} = \frac{x^{(2)}}{2!}$$

$$E_3(x) = \frac{x^3}{6} - \frac{x^2}{4} + \frac{1}{24}, \quad E_4(x) = \frac{x^4}{24} - \frac{x^3}{12} + \frac{x}{24}$$

$$E_5(x) = \frac{x^5}{120} - \frac{x^4}{48} + \frac{x^2}{48} - \frac{1}{240}$$

From (47) $E_n(0) = e_n$ and from (46) $E_n(1) + E_n(0) = 0$. Hence $E_n(1) = -e_n$. This fact may aid in checking any particular $E_n(x)$.

If in (46) we let $x = -1$ we obtain

$$\frac{1}{2}[E_n(0) + E_n(-1)] = \frac{(-1)^n}{n!}$$

which simplified leads to

$$E_n(-1) = (-1)^n \frac{2}{n!} - e_n$$

Also we note that

$$E_n\left(\frac{1}{2}\right) = \sum_{i=0}^{n} \frac{e_i}{2^{n-i}(n-i)!}$$

From (48) we have

$$\int_0^1 E_n(x)\, dx = E_{n+1}(x) + k \Big]_0^1$$

$$= E_{n+1}(1) - E_{n+1}(0)$$

$$= -e_{n+1} - e_{n+1} = -2e_{n+1}$$

The Euler polynomials, $E_i(x)$, may also be obtained from the expansion

$$\frac{2e^{tx}}{e^t + 1} = E_0(x) + E_1(x)t + E_2(x)t^2 - \cdots = \sum_{i=0}^{\infty} E_i(x)t^i$$

by equating coefficients of like powers of t. In the left-hand member e is the base of our natural system of logarithms.

Also the coefficients, e_i, may be obtained from the expansion

$$\frac{2}{e^t + 1} = \sum_{i=0}^{\infty} e_i t^i$$

by equating like powers of t.

The coefficients e_i are in themselves not so important in mathematical analysis but certain numbers with which they are associated are encountered.

Thus, consider the expansion of $\tan x$:

$$\tan x = x + \tfrac{1}{3}x^3 + \tfrac{2}{15}x^5 + \tfrac{17}{315}x^7 + \tfrac{62}{2835}x^9 + \cdots$$

which we write in the form

$$\tan x = x + 2 \cdot \frac{x^3}{3!} + 16 \cdot \frac{x^5}{5!} + 272 \cdot \frac{x^7}{7!} + 7936 \cdot \frac{x^9}{9!} + \cdots$$

The numbers 1, 2, 16, 272, 7936, etc., which are coefficients of $x^i/i!$ are called tangent numbers. They may be represented by

$$T_n = \left| 2^n \cdot n! e_n \right|$$

Thus

$$T_1 = \left| 2 \cdot 1 \cdot (-\tfrac{1}{2}) \right| = 1$$

$$T_2 = \left| 2^2 \cdot 2!(0) \right| = 0$$

$$T_3 = \left| 2^3 \cdot 3!(\tfrac{1}{24}) \right| = 2$$

$$T_5 = \left| 2^5 \cdot 5!(-\tfrac{1}{240}) \right| = 16$$

$$T_7 = \left| 2^7 \cdot 7! \left(\frac{17}{40,320} \right) \right| = 272$$

$$T_9 = \left| 2^9 \cdot 9! \left(\frac{-31}{725,760} \right) \right| = 7936$$

and so on.

The coefficients, e_i, are also used in what are known as the Euler numbers, E_n, which are defined by the equation

$$E_n = 2^n \cdot n! E_n(\tfrac{1}{2})$$

That is, in (47) we substitute $x = \tfrac{1}{2}$ for $n = 1, 2, 3, \cdots$, etc., and thus determine $E_n(\tfrac{1}{2})$. The product of these values by $2^n \cdot n!$ gives us E_n. The following table gives in detail the steps in computing the Euler numbers. It can be shown that $E_n(\tfrac{1}{2}) = 0$ when n is odd.

TABLE 9.   EULER NUMBERS

n	$E_n(\tfrac{1}{2})$	$2^n \cdot n!$	$E_n = 2^n \cdot n! E_n(\tfrac{1}{2})$
0	1	1	$E_0 = 1$
1	0	2	$E_1 = 0$
2	$-\tfrac{1}{8}$	8	$E_2 = -1$
3	0	48	$E_3 = 0$
4	$\tfrac{5}{384}$	384	$E_4 = 5$
5	0	$32(120)$	$E_5 = 0$
6	$\dfrac{-61}{46{,}080}$	$64(720)$	$E_6 = -61$

The absolute values of E_n, $|E_n|$, are the coefficients of $x^n/n!$ in the expansion of sec x.   The expansion is thus

$$\sec x = 1 + \frac{x^2}{2} + 5 \cdot \frac{x^4}{4!} + 61 \cdot \frac{x^6}{6!} + \cdots = \sum_{i=0}^{\infty} (-1)^{2i} E_i \frac{x^{2i}}{(2i)!}$$

The numbers E_n also appear as the coefficients of $x^n/n!$ in the expansion of sech x.   Thus

$$\operatorname{sech} x = 1 - \frac{x^2}{2!} + 5 \cdot \frac{x^4}{4!} - 61 \cdot \frac{x^6}{6!} + \cdots = \sum_{i=0}^{\infty} (-1)^i E_{2i} \frac{x^{2i}}{(2i)!}$$

The Euler polynomials can be expressed in terms of the Bernoulli polynomials and vice versa, but to consider this aspect is beyond the scope of this Introduction.   The student who wishes to pursue this topic more completely should consult the works by Jordan and Nörlund.

Chapter IV

INTERPOLATION. APPROXIMATE INTEGRATION

1. Introduction

Interpolation has been described by the Danish mathematician, T. N. Thiele, as "the art of reading between the lines of a table." In elementary mathematics *interpolation* denotes the process of computing *intermediate values* of a function from a set of given values of the function. When we attempt to obtain values outside the given abscissal range, the process is called *extrapolation*. If the mathematical law of the function is known, then, in order to interpolate missing terms we merely substitute in the mathematical formula. Thus, consider the following series of corresponding values of x and y:

x	0	1	2	3	4	5	6
y	1	4	9	16	25	36	49

It is obvious here that these values obey the law $y = (x + 1)^2$, and any desired value of y can be found from the formula. Thus, if $x = \frac{1}{2}$, $y = \frac{9}{4}$.

If the mathematical law were not evident we would call upon Newton's formula for aid

$$U_x = U_0 + x\Delta U_0 + \frac{x^{(2)}}{2!} \Delta^2 U_0 + \cdots + \frac{x^{(n)}}{n!} \Delta^n U_0$$

Differencing the given values of y we find y_0 and its leading differences to be: $y_0 = 1$, $\Delta y_0 = 3$, $\Delta^2 y_0 = 2$, the higher differences being zero.

$$U_{\frac{1}{2}} = 1 + \frac{1}{2}(3) + \frac{(\frac{1}{2})(\frac{1}{2} - 1)}{2!} \quad (2)$$

$$= 1 + \tfrac{3}{2} - \tfrac{1}{4} = \tfrac{9}{4}$$

Of course, when series of corresponding values of x and y are known, several methods are available for finding the approximate values of intermediate terms. We can plot the points on coordinate paper and draw a smooth curve through or very near the plotted points, and measure the ordinate of the curve for any abscissa. Further, we might be able to find an empirical formula connecting our variables, and then use this formula to compute intermediate values of the function for values of x that are within our given abscissal range.

Deriving the empirical formula and making use of it is a respectable analytical procedure, but, in general, to find such a formula is a laborious process. Of course, the graphical method is satisfactory if results can be read from the graph with the accuracy that is demanded.

Let y_x be a function that is defined by the given values $y_0, y_1, y_2, \cdots,$ y_n which it takes for x_i, $i = 0, 1, \cdots, n$. Let U_x denote an arbitrary function that has the same values as y_x for the values $x_0, x_1, x_2, \cdots, x_n$. The function U_x is called an interpolation function.

While U_x can take a variety of forms, it is usually a polynomial, since polynomials are our simplest functions. Thus, we assume

$$U_x = a_0 + a_1 x + a_2 x^2 + \cdots + a_n x^n$$

is the polynomial that passes through the points (x_0, y_0), (x_1, y_1), $\cdots,$ (x_n, y_n). Since $U_x = y_x$ for the given values x we have, $(U_{x_i} \equiv U_i, i = 1, 2, 3, \cdots, n)$,

$$U_0 = a_0 + a_1 x_0 + a_2 x_0{}^2 + \cdots + a_n x_0{}^n$$

$$U_1 = a_0 + a_1 x_1 + a_2 x_1{}^2 + \cdots + a_n x_1{}^n$$

$$\cdot \ \cdot \ \cdot \ \cdot \ \cdot \ \cdot \ \cdot \ \cdot \ \cdot \ \cdot \ \cdot \ \cdot \ \cdot \ \cdot \ \cdot$$

$$U_n = a_0 + a_1 x_n = a_2 x_n{}^2 + \cdots + a_n x_n{}^n$$

a system of $(n + 1)$ equations which determine $a_0, a_1, a_2, \cdots, a_n$.

2. Newton's Interpolation Formulas

To avoid solving the above equations we employ other but equivalent modes of procedure. In fact, we write the polynomial in the factorial form

$$U_x = A_0 + A_1 x + A_2 x^{(2)} + \cdots + A_n x^{(n)}$$

and determine the coefficients as we did in Chapter I, and arrive at Newton's formula

$$U_x = U_0 + x \Delta U_0 + \frac{x^{(2)}}{2!} \Delta^2 U_0 + \cdots + \frac{x^{(n)}}{n!} \Delta^n U_0 \qquad (1)$$

If some order of differences, say the kth order, is constant and higher orders vanish, then y_x is a polynomial of the kth degree and Newton's formula will give exact values of y. But generally the differences do not vanish, and then Newton's formula will give approximate values of y. In this formula $y_0 = U_0$ may be selected at any one of the tabulated values.

Example 1. Given the values of $\sin \theta$ for $\theta = 45°, 50°, 55°, 60°$, find $\sin 52°$.

Solution: We avoid decimals in the table by letting $U_x = 10^4 \sin (45 + 5x)$. Using the transformation $\theta = 5x + 45°$, when $\theta = 52°$, $x = 1.4$.

θ	x	U_x	ΔU_x	$\Delta^2 U_x$	$\Delta^3 U_x$
45°	0	7071	589	−57	−7
50°	1	7660	532	−64	
55°	2	8192	468		
60°	3	8660			

Assume $\Delta^3 U_x$ constant. This means that our interpolation function is a polynomial of degree three. Then

$$U_{1.4} = 7071 + 1.4(589) + \frac{(1.4)(1.4 - 1)}{2}(-57)$$

$$+ \frac{(1.4)(1.4 - 1)(1.4 - 2)}{3!}(-7)$$

$$= 7071 + 824.6 - 15.96 + 0.392$$

$$= 7880.032$$

Therefore, $\sin 52 = 0.7880$ to four places. The correct seven-place value is 0.7880108.

Example 2. The values of

$$U_t = \frac{1}{\sqrt{2\pi}} \int_0^t e^{-t^2/2}\, dt$$

are given at intervals of $t = 0.5$ from $t = 0$ to $t = 3$ in Table 10. Find the value of U_t when $t = 1.22$.

TABLE 10

t	x	U_x	ΔU_x	$\Delta^2 U_x$	$\Delta^3 U_x$	$\Delta^4 U_x$	$\Delta^5 U_x$
0.00	-2	0.00000	0.19146	-0.04158	-0.01645	0.02669	-0.01666
0.50	-1	0.19146	0.14988	-0.05803	0.01024	0.01003	-0.01446
1.00	0	0.34134	0.09185	-0.04779	0.02027	-0.00443	
1.50	1	0.43319	0.04406	-0.02752	0.01584		$-0.03112 \div 2$
2.00	2	0.47725	0.01654	-0.01168			$= -0.01556$
2.50	3	0.49379	0.00486				
3.00	4	0.49865					

In this problem the interpolated value sought is at $t = 1.22$ which is near the center of the table. In order that the values of U_x above and below this value may exert a larger influence, we choose $x = 0$ at $t = 1$. Further, in order to have equidistant ordinates at *unit* intervals we let $x = 2t - 2$. When $t = 1.22$, $x = 0.44$. Recalling that U_0 and its leading differences are found in a horizontal difference table in a horizontal line leading from $x = 0$, we have upon substitution in Newton's formula

$$U_{0.44} = 0.34134 + 0.44(0.09185) + \frac{(0.44)^{(2)}}{2!}(-0.04779)$$

$$+ \frac{(0.44)^{(3)}}{3!}(0.02027) + \frac{(0.44)^{(4)}}{4!}(-0.00443)$$

$$+ \frac{(0.44)^{(5)}}{5!}(-0.00156)$$

$$= 0.34134 + 0.04041 + 0.00589 + 0.00130$$

$$+ 0.00018 - 0.00045$$

$$= 0.38867$$

The true value is 0.38877, hence the error is 0.0001.

In our application of Newton's formula (1), hereinafter called Newton's Forward Interpolation Formula, our value of x was chosen near the beginning of the tabulated values, or in such a way that the values of U involved were the given values $U_0, U_1, U_2, \cdots, U_n$. This is clearly seen by referring to Table 4 of Chapter I, where we note that

$$\Delta U_0 = U_1 - U_0, \quad \Delta^2 U_0 = U_2 - 2U_1 + U_0,$$

$$\Delta^3 U_0 = U_3 - 3U_2 + 3U_1 - U_0, \quad \text{etc.}$$

Thus, the values of U that are used in (1) are U_0 and other values of U forward. Hence, the name *Forward Interpolation Formula*. We selected our U_0 in such a way that our given values of U would be involved in determining the coefficients of the interpolating polynomial function U_x. In using formula (1), as has been stated previously, the starting point U_0 may be any tabulated value, but then the formula will contain only those values of U which come after the value selected as a starting point.

If the value of x for which we wish to determine U_x is near the end of the table we may not have all the required differences. (See Table 2, Chapter I.) To solve the problem proposed here we derive what is known as Newton's Backward Interpolation Formula.

$$U_x = U_0 + x\Delta U_{-1} + \frac{(x+1)^{(2)}}{2!} \Delta^2 U_{-2} + \frac{(x+2)^{(3)}}{3!} \Delta^3 U_{-3} + \cdots$$

$$+ \frac{(x+n-1)^{(n)}}{n!} \Delta^n U_{-n} \quad (2)$$

In this case we select U_0 at or near the end of the table.

TABLE 11

x	U_x	ΔU_x	$\Delta^2 U_x$	$\Delta^3 U_x$	$\Delta^4 U_x$	$\Delta^5 U_x$	$\Delta^6 U_x$
-6	U_{-6}						
		ΔU_{-6}					
-5	U_{-5}		$\Delta^2 U_{-6}$				
		ΔU_{-5}		$\Delta^3 U_{-6}$			
-4	U_{-4}		$\Delta^2 U_{-5}$		$\Delta^4 U_{-6}$		
		ΔU_{-4}		$\Delta^3 U_{-5}$		$\Delta^5 U_{-6}$	
-3	U_{-3}		$\Delta^2 U_{-4}$		$\Delta^4 U_{-5}$		$\Delta^6 U_{-6}$
		ΔU_{-3}		$\Delta^3 U_{-4}$		$\Delta^5 U_{-5}$	
-2	U_{-2}		$\Delta^2 U_{-3}$		$\Delta^4 U_{-4}$		
		ΔU_{-2}		$\Delta^3 U_{-3}$			
-1	U_{-1}		$\Delta^2 U_{-2}$				
		ΔU_{-1}					
0	U_0						

To derive formula (2) we let

$$U_x = A_0 + A_1x + A_2(x + 1)^{(2)} + A_3(x + 2)^{(3)} + \cdots + A_n(x + n - 1)^{(n)}$$

$$(3)$$

Differencing U_x n times successively, we have

$$\Delta U_x = A_1 + 2A_2(x + 1) + 3A_3(x + 2)^{(2)} + \cdots + nA_n(x + n - 1)^{(n-1)}$$

$$\Delta^2 U_x = 1.2A_2 + 2.3A_3(x + 2) + \cdots + (n - 1)nA_n(x + n - 1)^{(n-2)}$$

· ·

$$\Delta^n U_x = A_n(n!)$$

Now in U_x let $x = 0$; in ΔU_x let $x = -1$; in $\Delta^2 U_x$ let $x = -2$; and so on.   We find

$$A_0 = U_0, \quad A_1 = \Delta U_{-1}, \quad A_2 = \frac{\Delta^2 U_{-2}}{2!}, \quad \cdots, \quad A_n = \frac{\Delta^n U_{-n}}{n!}$$

Substituting these values in (3) we have (2).

A glance at Table 11 reveals that by taking U_0 at or near the end of the table, the required differences are those which occur on the line of the lower side of the triangle or on a line parallel to it.

Example 3.   Given the values of $\sin \theta$ for $\theta = 45°, 50°, 55°, 60°$, find $\sin 58°$.

Solution: To avoid decimals let $U = 10^4 \sin (60 + 5x)$.   Using $\theta = 5x + 60$, when $\theta = 58°$, $x = -0.4$.   When $\theta = 60°$, $x = 0$ so we take $U_0 = 10^4 \sin 60 = 8660$.   See Example 1, Section 1, of this chapter. $\Delta U_{-1} = 468$, $\Delta^2 U_{-2} = -64$, $\Delta^3 U_{-3} = -7$.   Hence

$$U_{-0.4} = 8660 - 0.4(468) + \frac{(0.6)^{(2)}}{2!}(-64) + \frac{(1.6)^{(3)}}{3!}(-7)$$

$$= 8660 - 187.2 + 7.68 + 0.448$$

$$= 8480.928$$

Therefore $\sin 58° = 0.8481$ to four places.

3. Formulas of Gauss, Stirling, and Bessel

With the aid of a difference table we can derive other useful interpolation formulas.

TABLE 12

x	U_x	ΔU_x	$\Delta^2 U_x$	$\Delta^3 U_x$	$\Delta^4 U_x$	$\Delta^5 U_x$	$\Delta^6 U_x$
-3	U_{-3}						
		ΔU_{-3}					
-2	U_{-2}		$\Delta^2 U_{-3}$				
		ΔU_{-2}		$\Delta^3 U_{-3}$			
-1	U_{-1}		$\Delta^2 U_{-2}$		$\Delta^4 U_{-3}$		
		ΔU_{-1}		$\Delta^3 U_{-2}$		$\Delta^5 U_{-3}$	
0	U_0		$\Delta^2 U_{-1}$		$\Delta^4 U_{-2}$		$\Delta^6 U_{-3}$
		ΔU_0		$\Delta^3 U_{-1}$		$\Delta^5 U_{-2}$	
1	U_1		$\Delta^2 U_0$		$\Delta^4 U_{-1}$		
		ΔU_1		$\Delta^3 U_0$			
2	U_2		$\Delta^2 U_1$				
		ΔU_2					
3	U_3						

From the diagonal difference table, Table 12, we have the following equalities:

$$\Delta^2 U_0 = \Delta^2 U_{-1} + \Delta^3 U_{-1}$$

$$\Delta^3 U_0 = \Delta^3 U_{-1} + \Delta^4 U_{-1} = \Delta^3 U_{-1} + \Delta^4 U_{-2} + \Delta^5 U_{-2}$$

and so on.

Substituting these values in Newton's formula (1) we have

$$U_x = U_0 + x\Delta U_0 + \frac{x^{(2)}}{2!} \Delta^2 U_{-1} + \frac{(x+1)^{(3)}}{3!} \Delta^3 U_{-1} + \frac{(x+1)^{(4)}}{4!} \Delta^4 U_{-2}$$

$$+ \frac{(x+2)^{(5)}}{5!} \Delta^5 U_{-2} + \frac{(x+2)^{(6)}}{6!} \Delta^6 U_{-3} + \cdots \quad (4)$$

This formula (4) is due to Gauss. It employs the odd differences just *below* the central line from U_0 and the even differences on the central line.

Another formula due to Gauss may be derived in a similar manner. We have

$$\Delta U_0 = \Delta U_{-1} + \Delta^2 U_{-1}$$

$$\Delta^3 U_{-1} = \Delta^3 U_{-2} + \Delta^4 U_{-2}$$

$$\Delta^5 U_{-2} = \Delta^5 U_{-3} + \Delta^6 U_{-3}$$

and so on.

Substituting in (4) we have

$$U_x = U_0 + x\Delta U_{-1} + \frac{(x+1)^{(2)}}{2!}\Delta^2 U_{-1} + \frac{(x+1)^{(3)}}{3!}\Delta^3 U_{-2}$$

$$+ \frac{(x+2)^{(4)}}{4!}\Delta^4 U_{-2} + \frac{(x+2)^{(5)}}{5!}\Delta^5 U_{-3} + \cdots \quad (5)$$

This formula employs the odd differences just *above* the central line through U_0 and the even differences on the central line.

The mean of (4) and (5) gives Stirling's well-known central difference formula:

$$U_x = U_0 + x\Delta U + \frac{x^2}{2!}\Delta^2 U_{-1} + \frac{(x+1)^{(3)}}{3!}\Delta^3 U$$

$$+ \frac{x}{4}\frac{(x+1)^{(3)}}{3!}\Delta^4 U_{-2} + \frac{(x+2)^{(5)}}{5!}\Delta^5 U$$

$$+ \frac{x}{6}\frac{(x+2)^{(5)}}{5!}\Delta^6 U_{-3} + \cdots \quad (6)$$

where

$$\Delta U = \tfrac{1}{2}[\Delta U_{-1} + \Delta U_0]$$

$$\Delta^3 U = \tfrac{1}{2}[\Delta^3 U_{-1} + \Delta^3 U_{-2}]$$

$$\Delta^5 U = \tfrac{1}{2}[\Delta^5 U_{-3} + \Delta^5 U_{-2}]$$

and so on.

Stirling's central-difference formula employs the mean of the odd differences above and below the central line and the even differences on the central line.

Bessel's interpolation formula may be derived as follows. We have from the table

$$\Delta^3 U_{-1} = \Delta^2 U_0 - \Delta^2 U_{-1}$$

$$\Delta^5 U_{-2} = \Delta^4 U_{-1} - \Delta^4 U_{-2}$$

$$\Delta^7 U_{-3} = \Delta^6 U_{-2} - \Delta^6 U_{-3}$$

and so on. Substituting these values in Gauss' formula (4) we have Bessel's formula:

$$U_x = U_0 + x\Delta U_0 + \frac{x^{(2)}}{2!}\Delta^2 U + \frac{1}{3}\frac{x^{(2)}}{2!}\left(x - \frac{1}{2}\right)\Delta^3 U_{-1}$$

$$+ \frac{(x+1)^{(4)}}{4!}\Delta^4 U + \frac{1}{5}\frac{(x+1)^{(4)}}{4!}\left(x - \frac{1}{2}\right)\Delta^5 U_{-2} + \cdots \quad (7)$$

where

$$\Delta^2 U = \tfrac{1}{2}[\Delta^2 U_{-1} + \Delta^2 U_0]$$

$$\Delta^4 U = \tfrac{1}{2}[\Delta^4 U_{-2} + \Delta^4 U_{-1}]$$

and so on.

Example 1. Apply Stirling's central-difference formula to find the value of U_t required in Example 2, Section 1, of this chapter.

$$\Delta U = \tfrac{1}{2}[\Delta U_{-1} + \Delta U_0] = \tfrac{1}{2}[0.09185 + 0.14988] = 0.120865$$

$$\Delta^3 U = \tfrac{1}{2}[\Delta^3 U_{-1} + \Delta^3 U_{-2}] = \tfrac{1}{2}[0.01024 - 0.01645] = -0.003105$$

$$U_{0.44} = 0.34134 + 0.44(0.120865) + \frac{(0.44)^2}{2}(-0.05803)$$

$$+ \frac{1.44(0.44)(0.44 - 1)}{6}(-0.003105)$$

$$+ \frac{0.44(1.44)(0.44)(0.44 - 1)}{24}(0.02669)$$

$$= 0.34134 + 0.05318 - 0.00562 + 0.00018 - 0.00017 = 0.38891$$

Example 2. Find the value of U_t in Example 2, Section 1, of this chapter when Bessel's formula is applied.

$$\Delta^2 U = \tfrac{1}{2}[\Delta^2 U_{-1} + \Delta^2 U_0] = \tfrac{1}{2}[-0.05803 - 0.04779] = -0.05291$$

$$\Delta^4 U = \tfrac{1}{2}[\Delta^4 U_{-2} + \Delta^4 U_{-1}] = \tfrac{1}{2}[0.02669 + 0.01003] = 0.01836$$

$$U_{0.44} = 0.34134 + 0.44(0.09185) + \frac{0.44(0.44 - 1)}{2}(-0.05291)$$

$$+ \frac{0.44(0.44 - 1)}{6}(0.44 - 0.5)(0.01024)$$

$$+ \frac{(1.44)(0.44)(0.44 - 1)(0.44 - 2)}{24}(0.01836)$$

$$+ \frac{(1.44)(0.44)(0.44 - 1)(0.44 - 2)}{120}(0.44 - 0.5)(-0.01666)$$

$$= 0.34134 + 0.04041 + 0.00652 + 0.00003 + 0.00042 + 0.000005$$

$$= 0.38873$$

which gives an error of 0.00004.

Exercises

1. Given

$$\log 3.14 = 0.496929$$
$$\log 3.15 = 0.498310$$
$$\log 3.16 = 0.499687$$
$$\log 3.17 = 0.501059$$

find $\log \pi$ if $\pi = 3.1416$.

2. The values of e^{-t} for certain equidistant values of t are given in the following table. Find the value of e^{-t} when $t = 1.7489$.

t	e^{-t}
1.72	0.179 066 16
1.73	0.177 284 41
1.74	0.175 520 40
1.75	0.173 773 94
1.76	0.172 044 86
1.77	0.170 332 99
1.78	0.168 638 15

3. The amount of 1 in 50 years at compound interest

$$\text{at } 2\tfrac{1}{2} \text{ per cent} = 3.437\ 1087$$
$$\text{at } 3 \ \text{ per cent} = 4.383\ 9060$$
$$\text{at } 3\tfrac{1}{2} \text{ per cent} = 5.584\ 9269$$
$$\text{at } 4 \ \text{ per cent} = 7.106\ 6833$$

Find the amount at $3\tfrac{3}{4}$ per cent.

4. EQUIDISTANT TERMS WITH TERMS MISSING

By the method of operators or the method of induction we can establish that

$$\Delta^n U_x = U_{x+n} - n U_{x+n-1} + \frac{n^{(2)}}{2!} U_{x+n-2} - \frac{n^{(3)}}{3!} U_{x+n-3}$$
$$+ \cdots + (-1)^n U_x \quad (8)$$

If we have given several corresponding values of x and U_x we can find the missing terms by using formula (8).

Example 1. Given $U_0 = 148$, $U_1 = 192$, $U_2 = 241$, $U_4 = 374$, to find U_3.

Solution: Our four sets of values would determine a polynomial of degree 3. Hence $\Delta^3 U_x$ is assumed to be constant and $\Delta^4 U_x = 0$. In formula (8) let $x = 0$, and $n = 4$. Then

$$\Delta^4 U_0 = U_4 - 4U_3 + 6U_2 - 4U_1 + U_0 = 0$$

$$U_3 = \frac{U_4 + 6U_2 - 4U_1 + U_0}{4}$$

$$= \frac{374 + 6(241) - 4(192) + 148}{4}$$

$$= 300$$

Example 2.   Given $U_1 = 386$, $U_3 = 530$, $U_5 = 810$, find U_2 and U_4.

Solution: The three sets of values determine a quadratic polynomial. Hence $\Delta^3 U_x = 0$.
    Let

$$x = 1 \text{ and } n = 3: \quad \Delta^3 U_1 = U_4 - 3U_3 + 3U_2 - U_1 = 0$$

$$x = 2 \text{ and } n = 3: \quad \Delta^3 U_2 = U_5 - 3U_4 + 3U_3 - U_2 = 0$$

We thus have two equations in two unknowns, U_2 and U_4.   Substituting the given values and solving we obtain

$$U_2 = 441, \quad U_4 = 533$$
$$653$$

5. LAGRANGE'S INTERPOLATION FORMULA

The interpolation formulas derived and applied in the preceding sections are based upon the assumption that the values of the independent variable are given at equidistant intervals.   We now derive a formula, due to Lagrange, which may be used when the increments of the independent variable are equal or unequal.
    Assume the following table of values of x and y, where $y = U_x$ for the given $(n + 1)$ values of x and where $U_{x_i} \equiv U_i$.   As usual U_x is the interpolating function for $y = f(x)$.

x	x_0	x_1	x_2	$x_3 \cdots x_{n-1}$	x_n
$y = U_x$	U_0	U_1	U_2	$U_3 \cdots U_{n-1}$	U_n

Let

$$U_x = A_0(x - x_1)(x - x_2)(x - x_3) \cdots (x - x_n)$$
$$+ A_1(x - x_0)(x - x_2)(x - x_3) \cdots (x - x_n)$$
$$+ A_2(x - x_0)(x - x_1)(x - x_3) \cdots (x - x_n)$$
$$\cdot \cdot \cdot \cdot \cdot \cdot \cdot \cdot \cdot \cdot \cdot \cdot \cdot \cdot \cdot \cdot \cdot$$
$$+ A_n(x - x_0)(x - x_1)(x - x_2) \cdots (x - x_{n-1}) \qquad (9)$$

Clearly each term of (9) is of degree n and hence (9) is a polynomial of degree n.   We determine the $(n + 1)$ constants A_0, A_1, A_2, $\cdots$, A_n by requiring the $(n + 1)$ given sets of values to satisfy (9).   Letting (x_0, U_0)

satisfy (9) we have

$$U_0 = A_0(x_0 - x_1)(x_0 - x_2)\cdots(x_0 - x_n)$$

and

$$A_0 = \frac{U_0}{(x_0 - x_1)(x_0 - x_2)\cdots(x_0 - x_n)}$$

Similarly, by letting (x_1, U_1), (x_2, U_2), $\cdots$, (x_n, U_n) each satisfy (9) we obtain

$$A_1 = \frac{U_1}{(x_1 - x_0)(x_1 - x_2)\cdots(x_1 - x_n)}$$

$$A_2 = \frac{U_2}{(x_2 - x_0)(x_2 - x_1)(x_2 - x_3)\cdots(x_2 - x_n)}$$

$$\cdot\ \cdot\ \cdot\ \cdot\ \cdot\ \cdot\ \cdot\ \cdot\ \cdot\ \cdot\ \cdot\ \cdot\ \cdot\ \cdot\ \cdot\ \cdot\ \cdot\ \cdot$$

$$A_n = \frac{U_n}{(x_n - x_0)(x_n - x_1)\cdots(x_n - x_{n-1})}$$

Substituting these values in (9) we obtain Lagrange's interpolation formula:

$$U_x = \frac{(x - x_1)(x - x_2)(x - x_3)\cdots(x - x_n)}{(x_0 - x_1)(x_0 - x_2)(x_0 - x_3)\cdots(x_0 - x_n)} U_0$$

$$+ \frac{(x - x_0)(x - x_2)(x - x_3)\cdots(x - x_n)}{(x_1 - x_0)(x_1 - x_2)(x_1 - x_3)\cdots(x_1 - x_n)} U_1$$

$$\cdot\ \cdot$$

$$+ \frac{(x - x_0)(x - x_1)(x - x_2)\cdots(x - x_{n-1})}{(x_n - x_0)(x_n - x_1)(x_n - x_2)\cdots(x_n - x_{n-1})} U_n \qquad (10)$$

Example: Given

$$\log 654 = 2.8156 \qquad \log 659 = 2.8189$$

$$\log 658 = 2.8182 \qquad \log 661 = 2.8202$$

find log 656.

Solution: To save labor let $t_i = x_i - 654$.
We then have

$x_0 = 654$	$t_0 = 0$	$U_0 = 2.8156$
$x_1 = 658$	$t_1 = 4$	$U_1 = 2.8182$
$x_2 = 659$	$t_2 = 5$	$U_2 = 2.8189$
$x_3 = 661$	$t_3 = 7$	$U_3 = 2.8202$
$x = 656$	$t = 2$	$U_t = (\quad)$

In formula (10) replace x by t, x_i by t_i, and

$$U_2 = \frac{(2-4)(2-5)(2-7)}{(0-4)(0-5)(0-7)}(2.8156) + \frac{(2-0)(2-5)(2-7)}{(4-0)(4-5)(4-7)}(2.8182)$$

$$+ \frac{(2-0)(2-4)(2-7)}{(5-0)(5-4)(5-7)}(2.8189)$$

$$+ \frac{(2-0)(2-4)(2-5)}{(7-0)(7-4)(7-5)}(2.8202)$$

$$= -\tfrac{3}{14}(2.8156) + \tfrac{5}{2}(2.8182) - 2(2.8189) + \tfrac{2}{7}(2.8202)$$

$$= \tfrac{1}{14}(8.4468 + 98.6370 - 78.9292 + 11.2808)$$

$$= \tfrac{1}{14}(39.4354) = 2.8168$$

The true value of log 656 is 2.8169 to four places.

Lagrange's formula is tedious to use and for accurate results the values of the independent variable should be taken close together.

6. CONCLUDING REMARKS ON INTERPOLATION

The interpolation functions that we have used are polynomials that coincide with the given function at the $(n + 1)$ points (x_0, y_0), (x_1, y_1), $\cdots$, (x_n, y_n). These $(n + 1)$ points determine a polynomial of degree n. Since these interpolating functions are polynomials, they may be differentiated and thus the values of derivatives of the unknown functions may be approximated for values of x in the given abscissal range.

The investigation of the relative accuracy of interpolation formulas would require a background that is not assumed in this book. The interested reader can find considerable help from Professor J. B. Scarborough's *Numerical Mathematical Analysis*, Chapter V. Also the books by Fort, Milne-Thomson, and Steffensen deal with this problem rather thoroughly.

Exercises

1. Prove by induction:

$$\Delta^n U_x = U_{x+n} - nU_{x+n-1} + \frac{n^{(2)}}{2!} U_{x+n-2} + \cdots + (-1)^n U_x$$

2. Given

$$\log 100 = 2.000\ 000\ 00$$
$$\log 101 = 2.004\ 321\ 37$$
$$\log 103 = 2.012\ 837\ 22$$
$$\log 104 = 2.017\ 033\ 34$$

find log 102.

3. The values of $\tan \theta$ for certain values of θ are given. Find the approximate values of $\tan 79°$ and $\tan 81°$.

θ	77°	78°	80°	82°
$\tan \theta$	4.3315	4.7046	5.6713	7.1154

Hint: Assume $\Delta^4 U_0 = 0$ and $\Delta^4 U_1 = 0$.

4. If all the terms, except U_5, of the sequence $U_1, U_2, U_3, \cdots, U_9$ be given, show that the value of U_5 is

$$\frac{56(U_4 + U_6) - 28(U_3 + U_7) + 8(U_2 + U_8) - (U_1 + U_9)}{70}$$

5. Given $U_3 = 40$, $U_5 = 170$, $U_7 = 336$, and $U_t = 200$, compute t correct to one decimal place.

6. Given $\log 350 = 2.54407$, $\log 351 = 2.54531$, $\log 352 = 2.54654$, $\log 354 = 2.54900$, find $\log 353$ by two methods.

7. Approximate Integration

The problem of approximate integration is that of finding the approximate area under a curve. If the curve has an analytic representation $y = f(x)$, the area bounded by the curve, the x-axis, and ordinates at $x = a$ and $x = b$ is given by

$$A = \int_a^b f(x)\, dx$$

assuming $f(x)$ is single valued and continuous over the interval. If the integration cannot be effected an approximate method is indicated.

If we merely know a set of values of $f(x)$ for given values of x, the problem is solved by representing the integrand by an interpolation formula and then integrating the formula between the desired limits. In this way we derive what is known as a *quadrature formula.*

Since we may choose the origin to suit our pleasure, the problem is reduced to one of finding the area under the interpolating curve between $(0, U_0)$ and (n, U_n). If the increment of the independent variable t is unity and the abscissas of the $(n + 1)$ points are $t = 0, 1, 2, 3, \cdots, n$, then

$$U_t = U_0 + t\Delta U_0 + \frac{t^{(2)}}{2!} \Delta^2 U_0 + \cdots + \frac{t^{(n)}}{n!} \Delta^n U_0 \qquad (11)$$

and the area bounded by the curve, the t-axis, and the extreme ordinates is given by

$$A = \int_0^n U_t\, dt$$

In general, however, the increment of the independent variable is not unity. In this case we divide the given interval into n equal parts and erect the $(n + 1)$ ordinates U_0, U_1, U_2, $\cdots$, U_n. These $(n + 1)$ points determine a polynomial of degree n which is our interpolating function.

If the given $(n + 1)$ points are (x_0, U_0), $(x_0 + h, U_1)$, $(x_0 + 2h, U_2)$, $\cdots$, $(x_0 + nh, U_n)$, as shown by the following table, we let $t = (x - x_0)/h$ or $ht = x - x_0$.

x	x_0	$x_0 + h$	$x_0 + 2h$	$x_0 + 3h$	$\cdots$	$x_0 + nh$
$t = \dfrac{x - x_0}{h}$	0	1	2	3	$\cdots$	n
$U_x = U_t$	U_0	U_1	U_2	U_3	$\cdots$	U_n

The area in the (x, U_x) coordinates

$$\int_{x_0}^{x_0+nh} U_x \, dx$$

becomes, since $h \, dt = dx$, the area in (t, U_t) coordinates

$$h \int_0^n U_t \, dt$$

That is, the area bounded by the curve, the x-axis, and the extreme ordinates is

$$A = \int_{x_0}^{x_0+nh} U_x \, dx = h \int_0^n U_t \, dt$$

$$= h \int_0^n \left(U_0 + t\Delta U_0 + \frac{t^{(2)}}{2!} \Delta^2 U_0 + \cdots \right) dt$$

$$= h \left[nU_0 + \frac{n^2}{2} \Delta U_0 + \left(\frac{n^3}{3} - \frac{n^2}{2} \right) \frac{\Delta^2 U_0}{2!} \right.$$

$$\left. + \left(\frac{n^4}{4} - n^3 + n^2 \right) \frac{\Delta^3 U_0}{3!} + \cdots \right] \tag{12}$$

From this general formula (12) we can obtain several well-known special formulas.

(a) *The Trapezoidal Rule.* In (12) let $n = 1$. Then we reject all terms after that containing ΔU_0. That is, we assume the curve between two points is a straight line. The area of the first trapezoid is by (12)

$$A_1 = h\left[nU_0 + \frac{n^2}{2}\,\Delta U_0\right]_{n=1} = \frac{h}{2}\,(U_0 + U_1)$$

Similarly, the area of the second trapezoid is

$$A_2 = h\left[nU_1 + \frac{n^2}{2}\,\Delta U_1\right]_{n=1} = \frac{h}{2}\,(U_1 + U_2)$$

and so on. For the nth trapezoid,

$$A_n = h\left[nU_{n-1} + \frac{n^2}{2}\,\Delta U_{n-1}\right]_{n=1} = \frac{h}{2}\,(U_{n-1} + U_n)$$

The approximate area under the curve is given by the sum of the areas of the n trapezoids

$$A = \sum_{i=1}^{n} A_i = \frac{h}{2}[U_0 + 2U_1 + 2U_2 + \cdots + U_n] \qquad (13)$$

This formula is known as the Trapezoidal Rule. If the interval h is small and the curve reasonably flat it gives fairly accurate results. Geometrically speaking, in using the rule we replace the graph of the given function by n segments of straight lines and replace the area under the graph by that of a polygon.

If the equation of the curve is known, the ordinates $U_0, U_1, U_2, \cdots, U_n$ are found by computation; otherwise they must be measured.

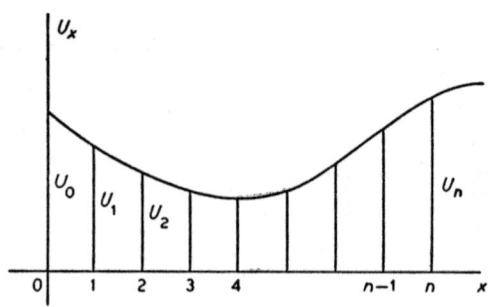

Example 1. Use the Trapezoidal Rule to find the approximate area under the curve $U_x = x^2$, using unit intervals, between ordinates at $x = 0$ and $x = 10$.

Solution: Here $h = 1$. We compute the ordinates as given in the table:

x	0	1	2	3	4	5	6	7	8	9	10
U_x	0	1	4	9	16	25	36	49	64	81	100

$$A = \tfrac{1}{2}[0 + 2(1 + 4 + 9 + 16 + 25 + 36 + 49 + 64 + 81) + 100]$$
$$= \tfrac{1}{2}(670) = 335$$

The true value is $\displaystyle\int_0^{10} x^2 \, dx = 333\tfrac{1}{3}$.

Example 2. A curve is determined by the points

x	0	0.5	1.0	1.5	2.0	2.5	3.0	3.5	4
U_x	23	19	14	11	12.5	16	19	20	20

of the table. Calculate the area bounded by the curve, the x-axis, and the extreme ordinates by the Trapezoidal Rule.

Here we have nine points given which will determine eight trapezoids, each with an altitude $h = 0.5$. Hence using (13)

$$A = \frac{0.5}{2}[23 + 2(19 + 14 + 11 + 12.5 + 16 + 19 + 20) + 20]$$

$$= \tfrac{1}{4}(43 + 223) = 66.5$$

(b) *Simpson's One-Third Rule.* This rule is established by assuming that the interpolating function is of degree 2. That is, through three consecutive points we pass a quadratic parabola $U_x = ax^2 + bx + c$, and thus neglect all differences beyond the second. In this case the number of strips must be *even* since a parabolic strip is substituted for each consecutive pair of trapezoidal strips.

In formula (12) replace n by 2 and the formula for the area bounded by a parabola through (x_0, U_0), $(x_0 + h, U_1)$, $(x_0 + 2h, U_2)$, the x-axis and the ordinates U_0 and U_2 is given by

$$\int_{x_0}^{x_0 + 2h} U_x \, dx = h\left[2U_0 + 2\Delta U_0 + \left(\frac{8}{3} - 2\right)\frac{\Delta^2 U_0}{2}\right]$$

Recalling that $\Delta U_0 = U_1 - U_0$, $\Delta^2 U_0 = U_2 - 2U_1 + U_0$, we find the area to be

$$A_1 = \frac{h}{3}(U_0 + 4U_1 + U_2)$$

If we apply the same formula for the next portion of the curve, that is for the ordinates U_2, U_3, U_4, we find

$$A_2 = \frac{h}{3}(U_2 + 4U_3 + U_4)$$

Similarly, for the ordinates U_4, U_5, U_6 we get

$$A_3 = \frac{h}{3}(U_4 + 4U_5 + U_6)$$

and so on. Adding all such expressions we obtain where n is *even*

$$A = \frac{h}{3}[U_0 + 4(U_1 + U_3 + \cdots + U_{n-1})$$
$$+ 2(U_2 + U_4 + \cdots + U_{n-2}) + U_n] \quad (14)$$

This important formula is known as Simpson's One-Third Rule.

Example 3.   Solve Example 2 using the Simpson One-Third Rule.

Solution:

$$A = \frac{0.5}{3}[23 + 4(19 + 11 + 16 + 20) + 2(14 + 12.5 + 19) + 20]$$

$$= \frac{0.5}{3}[43 + 4(66) \times 2(45.5)] = 66.3$$

It may be noted that the Simpson One-Third Rule does not assume that a smooth curve has been drawn through all the points. The method of obtaining the formula has been to draw a number of disjointed parabolas. The curve through the first three points will not generally pass through any of the remaining points.

(c) *Simpson's Three-Eighths Rule.*   This rule is established by dividing the given area up into 3, 6, 9, 12, etc., strips and passing polynomials of the third degree through groups of four consecutive points. The first polynomial will be determined by $(x_0,\ U_0)$, $(x_0 + h,\ U_1)$, $(x_0 + 2h,\ U_2)$, $(x_0 + 3h,\ U_3)$. In this case we neglect all differences beyond the third. Recalling that $\Delta U_0 = U_1 - U_0$, $\Delta^2 U_0 = U_2 - 2U_1 + U_0$, $\Delta^3 U_0 = U_3 - 3U_2 + 3U_1 - U_0$, the area under the cubic through the first four points is obtained by setting $n = 3$ in formula (12):

$$A_1 = \frac{3h}{8}[U_0 + 3U_1 + 3U_2 + U_3]$$

For the next set of intervals $(x_0 + 3h,\ U_3)$, $\cdots$, $(x_0 + 6h,\ U_6)$ we obtain

$$A_2 = \frac{3h}{8}[U_3 + 3U_4 + 3U_5 + U_6]$$

Adding all such expressions we obtain

$$A = \Sigma A_i = \frac{3h}{8}[U_0 + 3(U_1 + U_2 + U_4 + U_5 + \cdots + U_{n-1})$$
$$+ 2(U_3 + U_6 + \cdots + U_{n-3}) + U_n] \quad (15)$$

which is known as Simpson's Three-Eighths Rule.

(d) *Weddle's Rule.* This rule is established upon the assumption that a polynomial of degree six is passed through seven points (x_0, U_0), $(x_0 + h, U_1)$, $\cdots$, $(x_0 + 6h, U_6)$. That is, the area is assumed subdivided into 6 12, 18, etc., divisions. We find the area under the curve for each set, add the results and thus obtain Weddle's Rule.

In formula (12) replacing n by 6 and omitting all differences beyond the sixth we obtain for the first set of six divisions

$$A_1 = h[6U_0 + 18\Delta U_0 + 27\Delta^2 U_0 + 24\Delta^3 U_0$$
$$+ \tfrac{123}{10}\Delta^4 U_0 + \tfrac{33}{10}\Delta^5 U_0 + \tfrac{41}{140}\Delta^6 U_0]$$

Here the coefficient of $\Delta^6 U_0$ differs from $\tfrac{3}{10}$ by $\tfrac{1}{140}$. If we replace $\tfrac{41}{140}$ by $\tfrac{42}{140}$ we commit an error of $\tfrac{1}{140}\Delta^6 U_0$. If, as is usually the case, $\Delta^6 U_0$ is small, the error committed is small. We therefore change the last term of A_1 to $\tfrac{3}{10}\Delta^6 U_0$, and replace all differences by their values in terms of the U's. We then obtain A_1 in the form

$$A_1 = \frac{3h}{10}[U_0 + 5U_1 + U_2 + 6U_3 + U_4 + 5U_5 + U_6]$$

For the next set of 6 strips we obtain

$$A_2 = \frac{3h}{10}[U_6 + 5U_7 + U_8 + 6U_9 + U_{10} + 5U_{11} + U_{12}]$$

Adding all such expressions where n is a multiple of 6 we obtain

$$A = \Sigma A_i = \frac{3h}{10}[U_0 + 5U_1 + U_2 + 6U_3 + U_4 + 5U_5 + 2U_6$$
$$+ 5U_7 + U_8 + 6U_9 + U_{10} + 5U_{11} + 2U_{12}$$
$$\cdots \cdots \cdots \cdots \cdots \cdots \cdots \cdots \cdots \cdots$$
$$+ 2U_{n-6} + 5U_{n-5} + U_{n-4} + 6U_{n-3} + U_{n-2}$$
$$+ 5U_{n-1} + U_n] \quad (16)$$

which is known as Weddle's Rule.

Remarks. A study of the relative accuracy of the quadrature formulas would take us too far afield as it would assume upon the reader a background that this "Introduction" does not presuppose. The interested reader should consult the following works:

Scarborough: *Numerical Mathematical Analysis*, Chapter VIII.

Whittaker and Robinson: *The Calculus of Observations*, Chapter VII.

It may be stated however that Weddle's Rule is generally more accurate than any of the others. Of the two Simpson Rules, the One-Third Rule is the better.

Exercises

1. Evaluate $\int_0^2 \dfrac{dx}{1 + x^3}$ by Simpson's One-Third Rule using $h = \frac{1}{3}$.

2. Evaluate $\int_1^2 \sqrt{1 + x^3}\, dx$ by Simpson's One-Third Rule using $h = \frac{1}{4}$.

3. Evaluate $\int_0^1 \dfrac{dx}{1 + x^2}$ by Simpson's One-Third Rule with $h = \frac{1}{10}$ and thus compute the approximate value of π.

4. Find the approximate value of $\int_0^1 e^{-x^2}\, dx$ using Simpson's One-Third Rule with $h = \frac{1}{10}$.

(e) *The Euler-Maclaurin Sum Formula.* In our discussion of the Bernoulli Numbers we have found that they can be generated by the expansion

$$\frac{x}{e^x - 1} = \left[1 + \frac{x}{2!} + \frac{x^2}{3!} + \cdots\right]^{-1} = \sum_{i=0}^{\infty} \frac{B_i x^i}{i!}$$

Hence, we have

$$\left[1 + \frac{x}{2!} + \frac{x^2}{3!} + \frac{x^3}{4!} + \cdots\right]^{-1} = B_0 + B_1 x + \frac{B_2 x^2}{2!} + \frac{B_4 x^4}{4!} + \cdots$$

where $B_0 = 1$, $B_1 = -\frac{1}{2}$, $B_2 = \frac{1}{6}$, $B_3 = 0$, $B_4 = -\frac{1}{30}$, $B_5 = 0$, $B_6 = \frac{1}{42}$, $B_7 = 0$, $B_8 = -\frac{1}{30}$, $B_9 = 0$, $B_{10} = \frac{5}{66}$, $B_{11} = 0$, $B_{12} = -\frac{691}{2730}$.

We employ the above expansion to assist in the development of the Euler-Maclaurin Sum Formula which may be used either to find the approximate value of an integral or to approximate a sum of consecutive values of a function for equidistant values of x. These approximate values, it will be noted, require the values of certain derivatives of U_x for $x = 0$ and $x = n$.

In our previous work we have found that

$$\sum_0^{n-1} U_x = U_0 + U_1 + \cdots + U_{n-1} = \Delta^{-1} U_x]_0^n = V_x]_0^n = V_n - V_0$$

Since

$$V_x = \Delta^{-1}U_x = (e^D - 1)^{-1}U_x$$

$$= \left[D + \frac{D^2}{2!} + \frac{D^3}{3!} + \cdots\right]^{-1}U_x$$

$$= D^{-1}\left[1 + \frac{D}{2!} + \frac{D^2}{3!} + \cdots\right]^{-1}U_x$$

$$= D^{-1}\left[B_0 + B_1D + \frac{B_2D^2}{2!} + \frac{B_3D^3}{3!} + \cdots\right]U_x$$

$$= B_0D^{-1}U_x + B_1U_x + \frac{B_2}{2!}DU_x + \frac{B_4}{4!}D^3U_x + \cdots$$

by replacing in V_x the limits $x = 0$ and $x = n$ and recalling that $D^{-1}U_x = \int U_x\,dx$, we have

$$V_n - V_0 = V_x\rfloor_0^n = B_0\int_0^n U_x\,dx + B_1(U_n - U_0) + \frac{B_2}{2!}(U_n' - U_0')$$

$$+ \frac{B_4}{4!}(U_n''' - U_0''') + \frac{B_6}{6!}(U_n^v - U_0^v) + \cdots$$

Consequently, replacing the B's by their numerical values, we have the Euler-Maclaurin formula

$$\int_0^n U_x\,dx = U_0 + U_1 + \cdots + U_{n-1} + \frac{1}{2}(U_n -- U_0) - \frac{1}{12}(U_n' - U_0')$$

$$+ \frac{1}{720}(U_n''' - U_0''') - \frac{1}{30,240}(U_n^v - U_0^v) + \cdots \quad (17)$$

If the values of U_i in the above expression are collected, it will be observed that the above formula expresses the value of the integral given by the trapezoidal formula with certain other terms that may be looked upon as correction terms.

Example 4. Solve Example 1 by the Euler-Maclaurin formula.

Solution: $U_x = x^2$, $U_x' = 2x$.

$$\int_0^{10} x^2\,dx = (0 + 1 + 4 + 9 + 16 + 25 + 36 + 49 + 64 + 81)$$

$$+ \tfrac{1}{2}(100 - 0) - \tfrac{1}{12}(20 - 0)$$

$$= 285 + 50 - \tfrac{5}{3} = 333\tfrac{1}{3}$$

In formula (17) we have tacitly assumed that the values of x proceed by unit intervals. If the constant increment of x is h, we use $\dfrac{1}{e^{hD} - 1}$ as the generating function and arrive at the more general formula

$$\int_{x_0}^{x_0+nh} U_x \, dx = h \left[(U_0 + U_1 + \cdots + U_{n-1}) + \frac{1}{2} (U_n - U_0) \right]$$

$$- \frac{h}{12} (U_n' - U_0') + \frac{h^3}{720} (U_n''' - U_0''') - \frac{h^5}{30,240} (U_n^v - U_0^v) + \cdots$$

$$\tag{18}$$

Using the relations

$$D = \log (1 + \Delta) = \Delta - \tfrac{1}{2}\Delta^2 + \tfrac{1}{3}\Delta^3 - \tfrac{1}{4}\Delta^4 + \cdots$$
$$D^2 = \Delta^2 - \Delta^3 + \tfrac{11}{12}\Delta^4 - \tfrac{5}{6}\Delta^5 + \cdots$$
$$D^3 = \Delta^3 - \tfrac{3}{2}\Delta^4 + \tfrac{7}{4}\Delta^5 - \cdots$$

the Euler-Maclaurin formulas can be expressed in terms of differences instead of derivatives.

Example 5. Use the Euler-Maclaurin formula to find $\displaystyle\sum_{100}^{104} \frac{1}{x}$.

Solution: $U_x = \dfrac{1}{x}$, $U' = -\dfrac{1}{x^2}$, $U_x''' = -\dfrac{6}{x^4}$. Employing (17)

$$\int_{100}^{105} \frac{dx}{x} = \sum_{100}^{104} \frac{1}{x} + \frac{1}{2} \left[\frac{1}{105} - \frac{1}{100} \right] - \frac{1}{12} \left[-\frac{1}{105^2} + \frac{1}{100^2} \right]$$

$$+ \frac{6}{720} \left[-\frac{1}{105^4} + \frac{1}{100^4} \right]$$

$$\ln 1.05 = \sum_{100}^{104} \frac{1}{x} + \frac{1}{2} [0.009\ 5238 - 0.01] - 0.000\ 0008$$

$$0.048\ 7902 = \sum_{100}^{104} \frac{1}{x} - 0.002\ 389$$

$$0.049\ 0291 = \sum_{100}^{104} \frac{1}{x}$$

Example 6. Use the Euler-Maclaurin formula to find the value of

$$\frac{1}{201^2} + \frac{1}{203^2} + \cdots + \frac{1}{299^2}$$

Solution: $U_x = \dfrac{1}{x^2}$, $h = 2$, $n = 50$, $x_0 = 201$, $x_0 + nh = 301$.

Employing (18) we have

$$\int_{201}^{301} \frac{dx}{x^2} = 2\left[\frac{1}{201^2} + \frac{1}{203^2} + \cdots + \frac{1}{299^2}\right]$$

$$+ \left[\frac{1}{301^2} - \frac{1}{201^2}\right] - \frac{1}{6}\left[-\frac{2}{301^3} + \frac{2}{201^3}\right] + \cdots$$

$$-\frac{1}{x}\Big]_{201}^{301} = 2\left[\frac{1}{201^2} + \frac{1}{203^2} + \cdots + \frac{1}{299^2}\right]$$

$$+ \left[\frac{1}{301^2} - \frac{1}{201^2}\right] + \frac{1}{3}\left[\frac{1}{201^3} - \frac{1}{301^3}\right] + \cdots$$

$$\frac{1}{2}\left[\frac{1}{201} - \frac{1}{301}\right] + \frac{1}{2}\left[\frac{1}{201^2} - \frac{1}{301^2}\right] - \frac{1}{6}\left[\frac{1}{201^3} - \frac{1}{301^3}\right]$$

$$= \frac{1}{201^2} + \frac{1}{203^2} + \cdots + \frac{1}{299^2}$$

$$\left.\begin{array}{r} 0.000\ 826\ 433 \\ 0.000\ 006\ 858 \\ -0.000\ 000\ 001 \end{array}\right\} = \qquad ``$$

$$0.000\ 833\ 290 \quad = \qquad ``$$

Example 7. Use the Euler-Maclaurin formula to find the value of

$$1^p + 2^p + 3^p + \cdots + (n - 1)^p \text{ where } p \text{ is an integer} \geq 1$$

Solution: Employing (17) with $U_x = x^p$

$$1^p + 2^p + 3^p + \cdots + n^p = \int_0^n x^p\, dx + \frac{1}{2} n^p + \frac{B_2}{2!} pn^{p-1} + \cdots$$

where the right-hand member is discontinued at the last positive value of n. Transposing n^p to the right-hand member we have

$$\sum_{x=0}^{n-1} x^p = \frac{1}{p+1}\left[n^{p+1} + \binom{p+1}{1} B_1 n^p + \binom{p+1}{2} B_2 n^{p-1} + \cdots\right]$$

$$= \frac{1}{p+1}\left[(n + B)^{p+1} - B^{p+1}\right] \text{ symbolically.}$$

Exercises

1. Use the Euler-Maclaurin formula to show

(a) $\displaystyle\sum_1^n x^5 = \frac{n^2}{12}[2n^4 + 6n^3 + 5n^2 - 1]$.

(b) $\displaystyle\sum_1^n x^7 = \frac{n^2}{24}[3n^6 + 12n^5 + 14n^4 - 7n^2 + 2]$.

2. Show that $\displaystyle\sum_1^9 \frac{1}{x^3} = 1.196\ 532$.

3. Show that $\displaystyle\sum_{10}^{19} \frac{1}{x} = 0.718\ 7714$.

Chapter V

BETA AND GAMMA FUNCTIONS

1. Introduction

The integrals

1. $\beta(m, n) = \displaystyle\int_0^1 x^{m-1}(1 - x)^{n-1}\, dx$, and

2. $\Gamma(n) = \displaystyle\int_0^\infty x^{n-1} e^{-x}\, dx$

were first studied by Leonard Euler (1707–1783). In honor of Euler, Legendre gave these integrals the name Eulerian Integrals of the first and second kind. We call the functions Beta functions and Gamma functions. They are convergent when m and n are positive. Since the Beta function may be expressed in terms of the Gamma function, we shall first give attention to the second integral, the Gamma function.

2. The Gamma Function

The Gamma function is defined here by the integral

$$\Gamma(n) = \int_0^\infty x^{n-1} e^{-x}\, dx \tag{1}$$

$\Gamma(n)$ is defined above for any real value of n, except zero and negative integers. For positive integers we shall show:

$$\Gamma(n) = (n - 1)!$$

From the definition we have for $n = 1$,

$$\Gamma(1) = \int_0^\infty e^{-x}\, dx = -e^{-x}]_0^\infty = 0 + 1 = 1 \tag{2}$$

In order to investigate the properties of the Gamma function we shall first integrate by parts.

$$\int_0^t x^{n-1}e^{-x}\,dx = \int_0^t u\,dv = uv]_0^t - \int_0^t v\,du$$

Here

$$u = x^{n-1} \qquad\qquad dv = e^{-x}\,dx$$

$$du = (n-1)x^{n-2}\,dx \qquad\qquad v = -e^{-x}$$

Therefore

$$\int_0^t x^{n-1}e^{-x}\,dx = -t^{n-1}e^{-t} + (n-1)\int_0^t x^{n-2}e^{-x}\,dx$$

Using L'Hospital's Theorem, $(t^{n-1}e^{-t})$ approaches 0 as t becomes infinite. Therefore, we have, as t becomes infinite,

$$\Gamma(n) = \int_0^\infty x^{n-1}e^{-x}\,dx = (n-1)\int_0^\infty x^{(n-1)-1}e^{-x}\,dx \qquad (3)$$

The second integral we recognize as $\Gamma(n-1)$ so that we have

$$\Gamma(n) = (n-1)\Gamma(n-1) \qquad (4)$$

and replacing n by $(n+1)$ we have

$$\Gamma(n+1) = n\Gamma(n)$$

$$\Gamma(n) = \frac{\Gamma(n+1)}{n} \qquad\qquad (5)$$

By repeated use of (4)

$$\Gamma(n) = (n-1)\Gamma(n-1) = (n-1)(n-2)\Gamma(n-2)$$

$$= (n-1)(n-2)(n-3)\cdots 3\cdot 2\cdot 1\cdot\Gamma(1) = (n-1)!$$

since from (2), $\Gamma(1) = 1$. Therefore $\Gamma(n) = (n-1)!$ if n is a positive integer.

Tables [1] are available that give values of $\Gamma(n)$ for $1 < n < 2$, and by the use of these and the formulas (4) and (5) we can compute $\Gamma(n)$ for any positive value of n.

Example 1. Using (4)

$$\Gamma(3.2) = (2.2)\Gamma(2.2) = (2.2)(1.2)\Gamma(1.2)$$

$$= (2.2)(1.2)(0.9182) = 2.424$$

[1] See, for example, Rosenbach, Whitman, and Moskovitz, *Mathematical Tables*.

Example 2.   Using (5)

$$\Gamma(0.6) = \frac{\Gamma(1.6)}{0.6} = \frac{0.8935}{0.6} = 1.489$$

Let us now consider the Function $\Gamma(n)$ for $n < 0$. When $n < 0$, the integral (1) diverges (as will be shown later) and so fails to define a function. We can, however, extend the definition by means of (5). Let n lie in the interval $-1 < n < 0$. Then $\Gamma(n-1)$ may be defined for these values of n, if we agree to define $\Gamma(n)$ there by means of (5).

Thus, we can find $\Gamma(n)$ for negative values, except for negative integers, by this method.

Example 3.   Using (5)

$$\Gamma(-0.4) = \frac{\Gamma(0.6)}{-0.4} = \frac{\Gamma(1.6)}{(-0.4)(0.6)} = -3.723$$

From (1)

$$\Gamma(0.5) = \int_0^\infty z^{-0.5} e^{-z}\, dz$$

Let $z = x^2$, $dz = 2x\, dx$ and

$$\Gamma(0.5) = 2\int_0^\infty e^{-x^2}\, dx \tag{6}$$

Similarly

$$\Gamma(0.5) = 2\int_0^\infty e^{-y^2}\, dy \tag{7}$$

From (6) and (7)

$$[\Gamma(0.5)]^2 = 4\int_0^\infty \int_0^\infty e^{-x^2-y^2}\, dx\, dy$$

which is four times the volume in the first octant bounded by the surface

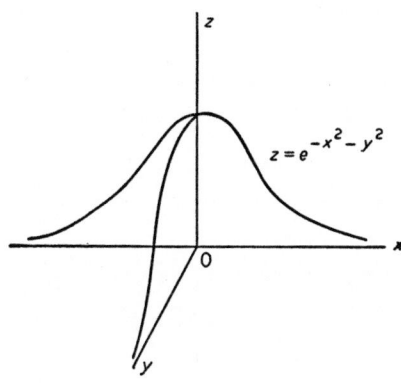

$z = e^{-x^2 - y^2}$ and the xy-plane. Changing to polar coordinates

$$[\Gamma(0.5)]^2 = 4 \int_0^\infty \int_0^{\frac{\pi}{2}} e^{-r^2} r \, dr \, d\theta = \pi$$

Therefore

$$\Gamma(0.5) = \sqrt{\pi}$$

We have previously stated that for $n = 0$ and $n =$ negative integers, $\Gamma(n)$ is undefined. We shall now show that this is true.

$$\int_0^\infty x^{n-1} e^{-x} \, dx = \int_0^a e^{-x} x^{n-1} \, dx + \int_a^\infty e^{-x} x^{n-1} \, dx, \text{ where } 0 < a < \infty$$

The first integral is perfectly regular, since it represents the area under the curve $y = e^{-x} x^{n-1}$, bounded by the lines $x = 0$, $x = a$, and the x-axis. The second integral is improper since the upper limit is infinite. But by definition, this means

$$\lim_{b \to \infty} \int_a^b e^{-x} x^{n-1} \, dx$$

This can be shown to converge; for, if x is sufficiently large, $e^{-x} x^{n-1} < \frac{1}{x^2}$, that is $e^x > x^{n+1}$. In detail the argument runs as follows: $y = e^{-x}$ decreases more rapidly than the power function x^{-k}, $(k > 0)$. Therefore, there must exist a point a, such that, for all values of $x > a$, $e^{-x} < x^{-k}$. Remembering that the definite integral represents an area under the curve and $y = e^{-x} x^{n-1}$ is always positive for $x > 0$,

$$0 < \int_a^b e^{-x} x^{n-1} \, dx < \int_a^b x^{n-1} x^{-k} \, dx$$

If $k = n + 1$, the second integral becomes

$$\int_a^b x^{-2} \, dx = -\frac{1}{x} \Big]_a^b = \frac{1}{a} - \frac{1}{b}$$

which has the limit of $\frac{1}{a}$ if $b \to \infty$. Thus

$$\int_a^\infty e^{-x} x^{n-1} \, dx = \lim_{b \to \infty} \int_a^b e^{-x} x^{n-1} \, dx < \frac{1}{a}$$

and therefore converges.

Now for $n = 0$

$$\Gamma(0) = \int_0^\infty e^{-x} x^{-1}\, dx = \int_0^1 e^{-x} x^{-1}\, dx + \int_1^\infty e^{-x} x^{-1}\, dx$$

Both of these are improper; the first because, when $x = 0$, the integrand becomes infinite, and the second has an infinite upper limit. The second integral can easily be shown to converge. Thus,

$$\int_1^\infty e^{-x} x^{-1}\, dx = \int_1^\infty \frac{e^{-x}}{x}\, dx = \lim_{h \to \infty} \int_1^h \frac{e^{-x}}{x}\, dx$$

Now

$$\frac{e^{-x}}{x} \leqq e^{-x} \quad \text{for } 1 \leqq x$$

Therefore,

$$\int_1^h \frac{e^{-x}}{x}\, dx < \int_1^h e^{-x}\, dx = -e^{-x}]_1^h = \left(-e^{-h} + \frac{1}{e}\right)$$

Since

$$\lim_{h \to \infty} \int_1^h \frac{e^{-x}}{x}\, dx < \frac{1}{e}$$

the second integral converges.

The first integral for $\Gamma(0)$ cannot be negative since the integrand is always positive for the range $0 < x < 1$. Moreover,

$$\frac{e^{-x}}{x} \geqq \frac{e^{-1}}{x} \quad \text{for } 0 < x \leqq 1$$

Consequently

$$\int_a^1 \frac{e^{-x}}{x}\, dx > \frac{1}{e} \int_a^1 \frac{dx}{x} = \frac{1}{e} (\log 1 - \log a)$$

and

$$\int_0^1 \frac{e^{-x} dx}{x} = \lim_{a \to 0} \int_a^1 \frac{e^{-x}}{x}\, dx > \lim_{a \to 0} \frac{1}{e} (\log 1 - \log a) = \infty$$

and hence $\Gamma(0) = \infty$.

It remains to define $\Gamma(n)$ for negative integral values of n. Equation (5) gives us $\Gamma(n) = \dfrac{\Gamma(n+1)}{n}$, and since

$$\Gamma(0) = \infty$$

it follows that

$$\Gamma(-1) = \frac{\Gamma(0)}{-1} = \infty$$

$$\Gamma(-2) = \frac{\Gamma(-1)}{-2} = \infty$$

and so on for $\Gamma(n)$, n a negative integer.

3. THE BETA FUNCTION

We now turn to the Beta function which is defined by

$$\beta(m, n) = \int_0^1 x^{m-1}(1 - x)^{n-1}\, dx \tag{8}$$

In the Beta function, m and n are positive, and $\beta(m, n)$ is always finite and determinate.

In $\displaystyle\int_0^1 x^{m-1}(1 - x)^{n-1}\, dx$, let $y = 1 - x$; then

$$\int_0^1 x^{m-1}(1 - x)^{n-1}\, dx = \int_0^1 y^{n-1}(1 - y)^{m-1}\, dy$$

and

$$\beta(m, n) = \beta(n, m) \tag{9}$$

We shall now develop the relation that connects the Beta and the Gamma functions.

In (1) let $x = z^2$, $dx = 2z\, dz$; then $\Gamma(n) = 2\displaystyle\int_0^\infty z^{2n-1}e^{-z^2}\, dz$. That is,

$$\Gamma(m) = 2\int_0^\infty e^{-x^2}x^{2m-1}\, dx \tag{10}$$

$$\Gamma(n) = 2\int_0^\infty e^{-y^2}y^{2n-1}\, dy$$

$$\Gamma(m)\Gamma(n) = 4\int_0^\infty\int_0^\infty e^{-x^2-y^2}x^{2m-1}y^{2n-1}\, dy\, dx \tag{11}$$

Considering (11) as a surface integral in the first quadrant, transforming to polar coordinates we obtain

$$\Gamma(m)\Gamma(n) = 4\int_0^\infty \int_0^{\frac{\pi}{2}} e^{-r^2} r^{2m-1}(\cos\theta)^{2m-1} r^{2n-1}(\sin\theta)^{2n-1} r\, dr\, d\theta$$

$$= 2\int_0^\infty e^{-r^2} r^{2(m+n)-1}\, dr \cdot 2\int_0^{\frac{\pi}{2}}(\cos\theta)^{2m-1}(\sin\theta)^{2n-1}\, d\theta \quad (12)$$

Referring to (10) the first integral of (12) is $\Gamma(m+n)$. We shall now show that $\beta(m, n)$, as defined by (8), may be transformed into the second integral of (12). To accomplish this, in (8) let $x = \cos^2\theta$, $(1-x) = \sin^2\theta$, $dx = -2\cos\theta\sin\theta\, d\theta$. Then

$$\beta(m, n) = \int_{\frac{\pi}{2}}^0 (\cos^2\theta)^{m-1}(\sin^2\theta)^{n-1}(-2\sin\theta\cos\theta\, d\theta)$$

$$= 2\int_0^{\frac{\pi}{2}}(\cos\theta)^{2m-1}(\sin\theta)^{2n-1}\, d\theta$$

Thus, from (12) we have

$$\Gamma(m)\Gamma(n) = \Gamma(m+n)\beta(m, n)$$

or

$$\beta(m, n) = \frac{\Gamma(m)\Gamma(n)}{\Gamma(m+n)} \quad (13)$$

4. Illustrative Examples

There are many integrals which are not in the form of our original equations that define Gamma and Beta functions, but by simple transformations they become forms of them.

Example 1. Consider $\int_0^{\frac{\pi}{2}} \sin^n x\, dx$, where n is greater than (-1).

$$\text{Let } y = \sin x, \quad dy = \cos x\, dx$$

$$dx = \frac{dy}{\cos x} = (1 - y^2)^{-\frac{1}{2}}\, dy$$

then

$$\int_0^{\frac{\pi}{2}} \sin^n x\, dx = \int_0^1 y^n(1 - y^2)^{-\frac{1}{2}}\, dy$$

Now let $z = y^2$, $dz = 2y\,dy$, $dy = \dfrac{dz}{2\sqrt{z}}$.

$$\int_0^1 y^n (1 - y^2)^{-\frac{1}{2}}\,dy = \frac{1}{2}\int_0^1 z^{\frac{n}{2} - \frac{1}{2}}(1 - z)^{-\frac{1}{2}}\,dz$$

$$= \frac{1}{2}\int_0^1 z^{\frac{n+1}{2} - 1}(1 - z)^{\frac{1}{2} - 1}\,dz$$

$$= \frac{1}{2}\beta\left(\frac{n+1}{2}, \frac{1}{2}\right) = \frac{\Gamma\left(\dfrac{n+1}{2}\right)\Gamma\left(\dfrac{1}{2}\right)}{2\Gamma\left(\dfrac{n+1}{2} + \dfrac{1}{2}\right)}$$

$$= \frac{\sqrt{\pi}}{2} \cdot \frac{\Gamma\left(\dfrac{n+1}{2}\right)}{\Gamma\left(\dfrac{n+2}{2}\right)}$$

Therefore,

$$\int_0^{\frac{\pi}{2}} \sin^n x\,dx = \int_0^1 y^n (1 - y^2)^{-\frac{1}{2}}\,dy = \frac{\sqrt{\pi}}{2} \cdot \frac{\Gamma\left(\dfrac{n+1}{2}\right)}{\Gamma\left(\dfrac{n+2}{2}\right)}$$

Example 2. Consider $\displaystyle\int_0^1 \frac{x^{2n}\,dx}{\sqrt{1 - x^2}}$.

$$\text{Let } x = \sin\theta \qquad\qquad x^{2n} = \sin^{2n}\theta$$

$$dx = \cos\theta\,d\theta \qquad\qquad x^2 = \sin^2\theta$$

$$\sqrt{1 - x^2} = \sqrt{1 - \sin^2\theta} = \cos\theta$$

$$\int_0^1 \frac{x^{2n}\,dx}{\sqrt{1 - x^2}} = \int_0^{\frac{\pi}{2}} \sin^{2n}\theta\,d\theta = \frac{\sqrt{\pi}}{2}\frac{\Gamma(n + \frac{1}{2})}{\Gamma(n + 1)}$$

from Example 1.

Example 3. Consider $\displaystyle\int_0^{\frac{\pi}{2}} \sin^n x \cos^m x\,dx$.

$$\text{Let } y = \sin x \qquad\qquad dy = \cos x\,dx$$

$$dx = (1 - y^2)^{-\frac{1}{2}}\,dy \qquad\qquad \cos x = (1 - y^2)^{\frac{1}{2}}$$

$$\int_0^{\frac{\pi}{2}} \sin^n x \cos^m x \, dx = \int_0^1 y^n (1 - y^2)^{\frac{m}{2} - \frac{1}{2}} \, dy$$

Now let $z = y^2$, $dz = 2y \, dy$, $dy = \dfrac{dz}{2\sqrt{z}}$. The above integral becomes

$$\frac{1}{2} \int_0^1 z^{\frac{n}{2} - \frac{1}{2}} (1 - z)^{\frac{m}{2} - \frac{1}{2}} \, dz = \frac{1}{2} \beta \left(\frac{n+1}{2}, \frac{m+1}{2} \right)$$

$$= \frac{1}{2} \frac{\Gamma\left(\dfrac{n+1}{2}\right) \Gamma\left(\dfrac{m+1}{2}\right)}{\Gamma\left(\dfrac{n+1}{2} + \dfrac{m+1}{2}\right)}$$

$$= \frac{1}{2} \frac{\Gamma\left(\dfrac{n+1}{2}\right) \Gamma\left(\dfrac{m+1}{2}\right)}{\Gamma\left(\dfrac{n+m}{2} + 1\right)}$$

Therefore,

$$\int_0^{\frac{\pi}{2}} \sin^n x \cos^m x \, dx = \int_0^1 y^n (1 - y^2)^{\frac{m-1}{2}} \, dy = \frac{1}{2} \beta \left(\frac{n+1}{2}, \frac{m+1}{2} \right)$$

$$= \frac{1}{2} \cdot \frac{\Gamma\left(\dfrac{n+1}{2}\right) \Gamma\left(\dfrac{m+1}{2}\right)}{\Gamma\left(\dfrac{m+n}{2} + 1\right)}$$

Example 4. Consider $\displaystyle\int_0^{\infty} x^n e^{-ax} \, dx$.

$$\text{Let } y = ax \qquad\qquad x = \frac{y}{a}$$

$$dy = a \, dx \qquad\qquad dx = \frac{dy}{a}$$

$$\int_0^{\infty} x^n e^{-ax} \, dx = \int_0^{\infty} \frac{y^n}{a^n} e^{-y} \frac{dy}{a} = \frac{1}{a^{n+1}} \int_0^{\infty} y^n e^{-y} \, dy = \frac{\Gamma(n+1)}{a^{n+1}}$$

Example 5. Show that $\Gamma(n) = \int_0^1 \left(\log \frac{1}{y} \right)^{n-1} dy$.

$$\text{Let } x = \log \frac{1}{y} = -\log y \qquad\qquad dy = -y\, dx$$

$$dx = -\frac{1}{y}\, dy \qquad\qquad\qquad dy = -e^{-x}\, dx$$

$$\int_0^1 \left(\log \frac{1}{y} \right)^{n-1} dy = \int_\infty^0 x^{n-1}(-e^{-x})\, dx = \int_0^\infty x^{n-1}e^{-x}\, dx = \Gamma(n)$$

Example 6. Consider the integral $\displaystyle\int_0^1 \frac{dx}{\sqrt{1-x^n}}$.

$$\text{Let } y = x^n$$

$$dy = nx^{n-1}\, dx$$

$$dx = \frac{dy}{nx^{n-1}} = \frac{dy}{ny^{1-\frac{1}{n}}}$$

$$\int_0^1 \frac{dx}{\sqrt{1-x^n}} = \frac{1}{n}\int_0^1 y^{\frac{1}{n}-1}(1-y)^{\frac{1}{2}-1}\, dy = \frac{1}{n}\beta\left(\frac{1}{n},\frac{1}{2}\right) = \frac{\sqrt{\pi}\,\Gamma\left(\frac{1}{n}\right)}{n\Gamma\left(\frac{1}{n}+\frac{1}{2}\right)}$$

Example 7. Evaluate $\displaystyle\int_0^\infty e^{-x^2}\, dx$.

$$\text{Let } y = x^2,\ dy = 2x\, dx,\ dx = \frac{dy}{2\sqrt{y}}.$$

$$\int_0^\infty e^{-x^2}\, dx = \frac{1}{2}\int_0^\infty y^{\frac{1}{2}-1}e^{-y}\, dy = \frac{\Gamma(\frac{1}{2})}{2} = \frac{\sqrt{\pi}}{2}$$

Exercises

1. Prove: $\displaystyle\int_0^1 x^m(-\log x)^n\, dx = \frac{\Gamma(n+1)}{(m+1)^{n+1}}$, $\ -1 < m,\ -1 < n$.

   Hint: In Example 5 let $y = x^{m+1}$.

2. Prove: $1 \cdot 3 \cdot 5 \cdot \ \cdots\ \cdot (2n-1) = \dfrac{2^n \Gamma(n+\frac{1}{2})}{\sqrt{\pi}}$.

3. Compute: $\displaystyle\int_0^1 \sqrt[3]{x}(-\log x)\, dx$.

4. Sketch the graph of $y = \Gamma(x)$.

5. Prove: $\displaystyle\int_0^{\frac{\pi}{2}} \sin^n 2x\, dx = \dfrac{2^{n-1}\left[\Gamma\dfrac{(n+1)}{2}\right]^2}{\Gamma(n+1)}$.

6. Prove: $\displaystyle\int_0^{\frac{\pi}{2}} \sin^n x\, dx = \int_0^{\frac{\pi}{2}} \cos^n x\, dx = \dfrac{1}{2}\beta\left(\dfrac{n+1}{2}, \dfrac{1}{2}\right)$.

7. Prove: $2\cdot4\cdot6\cdot8\cdot\ \cdots\ \cdot2n = 2^n\Gamma(n+1)$.

8. Prove: $x^{(n)} = \dfrac{\Gamma(x+1)}{\Gamma(x-n+1)}$.

9. Prove that the binomial coefficient $\dbinom{x}{n}$ equals $\dfrac{\Gamma(x+1)}{\Gamma(n+1)\Gamma(x-n+1)}$.

10. Show that $\displaystyle\int_0^1 \dfrac{dx}{\sqrt{1-x^{\frac{1}{4}}}} = \dfrac{128}{35}$.

11. Show that

(a) $\beta(x+1, y) = \dfrac{x}{x+y}\beta(x, y)$.

(b) $\beta(x, y+1) = \dfrac{y}{x+y}\beta(x, y)$.

12. Show that $\Delta_x\beta(x, y) = \dfrac{-y}{x+y}\beta(x, y) = -\beta(x, y+1)$.

13. Show that $\beta(n+1, y) = \dfrac{n!}{y(y+1)(y+2)\cdots(y+n)}$.

14. Prove: $\Delta^m \dfrac{1}{x+1} = (-1)^m\beta(x+1, m+1)$.

15. By repeated integration by parts prove $\beta(m, n) = \dfrac{\Gamma(m)\Gamma(n)}{\Gamma(m+n)}$.

16. Show that $\displaystyle\int_0^{\frac{\pi}{2}} \sin^5 x \cos^6 x\, dx = \dfrac{8}{693}$.

17. Show that $\displaystyle\int_0^{\frac{\pi}{2}} \sin^8 x\, dx = \dfrac{35\pi}{256}$.

Chapter VI

DIFFERENCE EQUATIONS

---

1. Introduction

An equation which expresses a relation between an independent variable x and successive differences or successive values of a dependent variable U_x is called a difference equation. Thus,

$$\text{(a)} \quad \Delta^3 U_x + \Delta^2 U_x - \Delta U_x - U_x = 0$$
$$\text{(b)} \quad 2U_x + 3\Delta U_x - \Delta^3 U_x = x$$

are illustrations of difference equations.

By means of the relationships

$$\Delta U_x = U_{x+1} - U_x$$

$$\Delta^2 U_x = U_{x+2} - 2U_{x+1} + U_x$$

$$\Delta^3 U_x = U_{x+3} - 3U_{x+2} + 3U_{x+1} - U_x$$

$$\cdots\cdots\cdots\cdots\cdots\cdots\cdots\cdots\cdots\cdots\cdots\cdots$$

$$\Delta^n U_x = U_{x+n} - nU_{x+n-1} + \frac{n^{(2)}}{2!} U_{x+n-2} + \cdots + (-1)^n U_x$$

we may express the difference equations in forms involving successive values of U_x instead of successive differences of U_x. Thus, the above illustrative difference equations (a) and (b) may be written

$$U_{x+3} - 2U_{x+2} = 0$$

$$U_{t+1} - 3U_t = 2 - t, \quad t = x + 2$$

If the equation is expressed in a form involving successive values of U_x, by means of the relationships

$$U_{x+1} = U_x + \Delta U_x$$

$$U_{x+2} = U_x + 2\Delta U_x + \Delta^2 U_x$$

$$U_{x+3} = U_x + 3\Delta U_x + 3\Delta^2 U_x + \Delta^3 U_x$$

. . . .

$$U_{x+n} = U_x + n\Delta U_x + \frac{n^{(2)}}{2}\Delta^2 U_x + \cdots + \Delta^n U_x$$

we may express the equation in a form involving successive differences of U_x. Of the two forms, for purposes of solution, that involving successive values is usually preferable.

If, besides U_x, the equation involves U_{x+m}, but no U with a greater index than $x + m$, the equation is said to be of order m. Thus,

$$U_{x+3} - 2U_{x+2} = 0$$

by setting $U_{x+2} = Z_x$, becomes

$$Z_{x+1} - 2Z_x = 0$$

and is, therefore, of the first order.

Similarly,
$$U_{x+1} - 3U_x = 2 + x$$

is of the first order, whereas

$$U_{x+2} + 5U_{x+1} + 4U_x = x^3$$
is of order two.

2. Solution of a Difference Equation

A solution of a difference equation is a relation connecting the independent and the dependent variables which satisfies the equation. Thus,

$$U_x = C_x 2^x$$

is a solution of the equation

$$U_{x+1} = 2U_x$$

if C_x is an arbitrary constant or an arbitrary periodic function of period 1. For substituting the given value of U_x we have, C_x assumed periodic,

$$C_{x+1} 2^{x+1} = 2C_x 2^x$$

or
$$C_{x+1} 2^{x+1} - C_x 2^{x+1} = 0$$

$$2^{x+1}(C_{x+1} - C_x) = 0$$

$$0 = 0$$

and the equation is satisfied.

Similarly
$$U_x = A_x 3^x + B_x 4^x$$

is a solution of
$$U_{x+2} - 7U_{x+1} + 12U_x = 0$$

if A_x and B_x are arbitrary constants or periodic functions of period 1.

A_x and B_x assumed periodic, we have

$$U_{x+2} = \quad 9A_{x+2}3^x + 16B_{x+2}4^x$$

$$-7U_{x+1} = -21A_{x+1}3^x - 28B_{x+1}4^x$$

$$12U_x \quad = \quad 12A_x 3^x \quad + 12B_x 4^x$$

Sum $= 3^x(9A_{x+2} - 21A_{x+1} + 12A_x) + 4^x(16B_{x+2} - 28B_{x+1} + 12B_x)$

The coefficient of 3^x in the above expression can be written in the form

$$9(A_{x+2} - A_{x+1}) - 12(A_{x+1} - A_x)$$

which is identically zero.

Similarly, the coefficient of 4^x is identically zero. Therefore, the given equation is satisfied by the given value of U_x.

We leave it an exercise for the student to show that the above illustrative examples are satisfied when C_x, A_x, and B_x are arbitrary constants C, A, and B.

Hereinafter, when we write constants C_1, C_2, A, B, etc., in connection with our solutions we assume they are expressions whose differences are zero.

It is thus seen that a difference equation may have an indefinite number of solutions. If the solution contains arbitrary constants equal in number to the order of the equation, it is the *general solution* or *complete primitive*. A solution which is derivable from the general solution by assigning fixed values to one or more of the arbitrary constants is called a *particular solution*. Thus, $C_1 3^x$ and $2(4^x)$ are particular solutions of $U_{x+2} - 7U_{x+1} + 12U_x = 0$.

Exercises

1. Show that $U_x = C_1 + C_2(6^x)$ is a solution of $U_{x+2} - 7U_{x+1} + 6U_x = 0$.

2. Show that $U_x = C_1(-1)^x + C_2(-3)^x + C_3(3)^x$ is a solution of

$$U_{x+3} + U_{x+2} - 9U_{x+1} - 9U_x = 0$$

3. Show that $C_1(-4 + 2\sqrt{3})^x + C_2(-4 - 2\sqrt{3})^x$ is a solution of

$$U_{x+2} + 8U_{x+1} + 4U_x = 0$$

4. Show that $U_x = 2^x \left(C_1 \cos \dfrac{2\pi x}{3} + C_2 \sin \dfrac{2\pi x}{3} \right)$ is a solution of

$$U_{x+2} + 2U_{x+1} + 4U_x = 0$$

3. Derivation of a Difference Equation from Its Primitive

Just as the process of integration is the inverse of that of differentiation, so the problem of finding the solution of a difference equation is the inverse of that of finding the difference equation which is satisfied by a relation among a set of variables. Thus, if $y_x = 3^x$, $\Delta y_x = 2(3^x) = 2y_x$, and $y_x = 3^x$ is a solution of the difference equation, $\Delta y_x = 2y_x$. Similarly, if $y_x = C_1 3^x$, $\Delta y_x = 2y_x$, and $y_x = C_1 3^x$ is the general solution of $\Delta y_x = 2y_x$, since it satisfies the equation and contains arbitrary constants equal in number to that of the order of the equation.

As another illustration, consider the expression

$$U_x = C_1 a^x + C_2 b^x$$

where C_1 and C_2 are arbitrary constants or periodic functions of x. It is easy to show that the above value of U_x satisfies the equation

$$U_{x+2} - (a + b)U_{x+1} + abU_x = 0$$

and is, thus, a complete primitive of it. Here the elimination of the two arbitrary constants leads to an equation of order two.

In general, if we have a relation which involves n arbitrary constants, it is possible by differencing the function n times to secure in all $n + 1$ equations from which to eliminate the n constants. Since the elimination process is unique, we see intuitively that *a primitive involving n arbitrary constants gives rise to a difference equation of the nth order.* The converse is also true, namely that *the solution* of an equation of order n generally *contains n arbitrary constants, $C_1, C_2, \cdots, C_n$.*

Exercises

1. Give the order of the following equations:

$$(1)\ \ U_{x+2} + 5U_{x+1} + 4U_x = x^3$$

$$(2)\ \ \Delta^2 U_x + 8\Delta U_x + 3U_x = \cos \pi x$$

$$(3)\ \ \Delta^3 U_x - 3\Delta U_x - 2U_x = x + 2$$

2. Find the difference equations for which the following are complete primitives or general solutions:

$$(1)\ \ U_x = C3^x + x3^{x-1}$$

$$(2)\ \ U_x = C_1 2^x + C_2 3^x$$

$$(3)\ \ U_x = C_1 + C_2 3^x$$

$$(4)\ \ U_x = (C_1 + C_2 x)3^x$$

$$(5)\ \ U_x = C_1 2^x + C_2 3^x + \tfrac{1}{2}$$

4. Solution of Simple Difference Equations

The solutions of many difference equations can be obtained by decidedly elementary processes. A mere change of form or a simple substitution may reduce the equation to an integrable form.

Example 1. Solve: $U_{x+1} - U_x = a^x$, $a \neq 1$.

Solution:

$$U_{x+1} - U_x = a^x$$

$$\Delta U_x = a^x$$

$$U_x = \Delta^{-1} a^x + C = \frac{a^x}{a-1} + C$$

If in this example, $a = 1$, then we have

$$\Delta U_x = 1$$

$$U_x = x + C$$

Example 2. Solve $\Delta^2 U_x = 2^x + x$.

Solution: Integrating we have

$$\Delta U_x = 2^x + \frac{x^{(2)}}{2} + C_1$$

$$U_x = 2^x + \frac{x^{(3)}}{6} + C_1 x + C_2$$

Example 3. Solve $U_{x+1} - aU_x = 0$.

Solution: Multiplying the equation through by the factor [1] a^{-x-1} we obtain

$$a^{-(x+1)} U_{x+1} - a^{-x} U_x = 0$$

or

$$\Delta a^{-x} U_x = 0$$

from which we obtain

$$a^{-x} U_x = C \quad \text{or} \quad U_x = Ca^x$$

Exercises

Solve the following equations:

1. $U_{x+1} - 2U_x = 3x$.   **2.** $U_{x+1} - 2U_x = 3^x$.

---

[1] The factor which, when multiplied into $f(x)$, makes the result integrable is called an *integrating factor* of $f(x)$. The result is then an *exact difference*.

3. $U_{x+1} - U_x = \sin \dfrac{\pi x}{3}.$

4. $\Delta U_x = \dfrac{1}{(x+1)^{|3|}}.$

5. $3U_{x+1} - U_x = x.$

6. $U_{x+1} - U_x = x,\ U_0 = 1.$

7. $\Delta U_x = (x^2 + 1)x!,\ U_0 = 1.$

8. $\Delta U_x = (2x - 1)3^x,\ U_0 = 0.$

5. Linear Equations of Order One

A linear equation of order one is an equation in the form

$$U_{x+1} - A_x U_x = B_x \tag{1}$$

where A_x and B_x are functions of x.

We shall first consider the simple case in which $B_x = 0$. We then have the *homogeneous* linear equation of order one

$$U_{x+1} - A_x U_x = 0 \tag{2}$$

From (2) it follows that

$$U_1 = U_0 A_0$$

$$U_2 = U_1 A_1 = U_0 A_0 A_1$$

$$U_3 = U_2 A_2 = U_0 A_0 A_1 A_2$$

$$\cdots \cdots \cdots \cdots \cdots$$

$$U_x = U_0 A_0 A_1 A_2 \cdots A_{x-1}$$

If we assign to U_0 the arbitrary value C, the solution to (2) becomes

$$U_x = C A_0 A_1 A_2 \cdots A_{x-1} = C \prod_{x=0}^{x-1} A_x \tag{3}$$

More generally,

$$U_x = C A_a A_{a+1} A_{a+2} \cdots A_{x-1}, \quad C = U_a$$

It is obvious that (3) may be written

$$\log U_x = \log C + \sum_{x=0}^{x-1} \log A_x$$

Example 1. Solve the equation

$$U_{x+1} - 3U_x = 0$$

First solution. Here $A_x = 3$, so that

$$A_0 = A_1 = A_2 = \cdots = A_{x-1} = 3$$

Substituting in (3) we have

$$U_x = C \prod_{x=0}^{x-1} 3 = C \cdot 3^x$$

Second solution. Taking the logarithm of the given equation to the base 3 we have

$$\log_3 U_{x+1} = \log_3 3 + \log_3 U_x$$

$$\log_3 U_{x+1} - \log_3 U_x = 1$$

$$\Delta \log_3 U_x = 1$$

$$\log_3 U_x = \Delta^{-1} 1 + C_1 = x + C_1$$

$$U_x = 3^{x+C_1} = C3^x$$

Third solution. Multiplying through by the integrating factor 3^{-x-1} we have

$$3^{-x-1} U_{x+1} - 3^{-x} U_x = 0$$

which is exact. It is

$$\Delta 3^{-x} U_x = 0$$

from which, upon integrating, we obtain

$$3^{-x} U_x = C$$

$$U_x = C3^x$$

Example 2. Solve the equation

$$U_{x+1} - x U_x = 0, \quad x > 0$$

Solution: Here $A_x = x$, and hence

$$A_1 = 1, \quad A_2 = 2, \quad A_3 = 3, \quad \cdots, \quad A_{x-1} = x - 1$$

Therefore by (3)

$$U_x = C \prod_1^{x-1} x = C(x-1)!, \quad C = U_1$$

Exercises

Solve the equations:

1. $U_{x+1} = 2^x U_x$, (a) by taking logarithms to the base 2, and (b) using (3).
2. $U_{x+1} - U_x = x^2$.
3. $U_{x+1} = 3^x U_x$ by two methods.
4. $x U_{x+1} - (x+1) U_x = 1$.
5. $U_{x+1} - x^2 U_x = 0$.
6. $(x+1) U_{x+1} - x U_x = x^3$.

To obtain the solution of (1), we let $U_x = Z_x V_x$, where Z_x and V_x are functions of x to be determined. We shall find that, if Z_x is a solution of (2), V_x can be determined and thus a solution of (1) is immediately effected. We have

$$Z_{x+1} V_{x+1} - A_x Z_x V_x = B_x$$

which, upon substituting,

$$V_{x+1} = V_x + \Delta V_x$$

reduces to

$$V_x(Z_{x+1} - A_x Z_x) + Z_{x+1}\Delta V_x = B_x \qquad (4)$$

If Z_x is a particular solution of (2), that is, if

$$Z_x = \prod_0^{x-1} A_x \qquad (5)$$

$Z_{x+1} - A_x Z_x$ vanishes identically and we obtain

$$Z_{x+1}\Delta V_x = B_x$$

from which V_x can be determined. We find

$$V_x = \Delta^{-1} \frac{B_x}{Z_{x+1}} + C \qquad (6)$$

and the solution of (1) becomes

$$U_x = Z_x V_x = CZ_x + Z_x \Delta^{-1} \frac{B_x}{Z_{x+1}} \qquad (7)$$

Consequently to solve (1) we first determine Z_x such that Z_x is a particular solution of (2). We then determine V_x from (6), and finally combine Z_x and V_x as in (7) to find U_x.

Example 3. Solve the equation

$$U_{x+1} - 3U_x = 2^x$$

Solution: Here $A_x = 3$, $B_x = 2^x$. Hence

$$Z_x = \prod_0^{x-1} 3 = 3^x$$

$$V_x = \Delta^{-1} \frac{2^x}{3^{x+1}} + C = \frac{1}{3}\Delta^{-1}\left(\frac{2}{3}\right)^x + C$$

$$V_x = -(\tfrac{2}{3})^x + C$$

$$U_x = Z_x V_x = C3^x - 2^x$$

Exercises

Solve the equations and verify your solutions.

1. $U_{x+1} - 3U_x = 3^x$.
2. $U_{x+1} - 3U_x = x$.
3. $U_{x+1} - 3U_x = x + 2^x$.

4. $U_{x+1} - aU_x = x + 2^x$.

5. $U_{x+1} - (x + 1)U_x = 0$.

6. $U_{x+1} - (x + 1)U_x = 2^x(x - 1)$.

7. $\Delta U_x + 2U_x = -x - 1$.

8. $U^2_{x+1} - 3U_{x+1}U_x + 2U_x{}^2 = 0$.

9. $U_{x+1} - aU_x = (2x + 1)a^x$.

10. $\Delta^3 U_x - 3\Delta U_x - 2U_x = -x$.

11. $U_{x+1} - aU_x = \cos nx$.

12. $s_{\overline{x+1}|} - s_{\overline{x}|} = (1 + i)^x$, $s_{\overline{1}|} = 1$.

13. $a_{\overline{x+1}|} - a_{\overline{x}|} = (1 + i)^{-x-1}$, $a_{\overline{0}|} = 0$.

14. If R dollars are deposited at the end of each year for x years in a savings bank at interest rate i, find the total amount in the fund at the end of the period.

    Hint: Show that $U_{x+1} = (1 + i)U_x + R$.

15. There are x points in a plane, no three of which are in the same straight line. Find the number of straight lines and the number of triangles formed by using the x points as vertices.

6. Linear Equations

An equation of the form

$$U_{x+n} + p_1 U_{x+n-1} + \cdots + p_n U_x = r_x \tag{8}$$

where p_i, $i = 1, 2, \cdots, n$, and r_x are functions of x, or constants, is called a linear difference equation. If the right-hand member, r_x, is zero the equation is called *homogeneous;* otherwise it is called *complete.*

The homogeneous equation is thus of the form

$$U_{x+n} + p_1 U_{x+n-1} + \cdots + p_n U_x = 0 \tag{9}$$

With regard to equation (9), the following theorems are easily established:

(a) If $U_1(x)$ is a solution of (9) so is $C_1 U_1(x)$.

(b) If $U_1(x)$ and $U_2(x)$ are solutions of (9) so is $C_1 U_1(x) + C_2 U_2(x)$.

(c) If $U_1, U_2, U_3, \cdots, U_n$ are n particular functions of x which are solutions of (9) then

$$C_1 U_1 + C_2 U_2 + \cdots + C_n U_n \tag{10}$$

is also a solution, the n functions being assumed linearly independent. In this case the n functions are called a *fundamental set,* and (10) is a complete solution of (9).

(d) If $C_1 U_1 + C_2 U_2 + \cdots + C_n U_n$ is a complete solution of (9) and Z_x is a particular solution of (8), then

$$U_x = C_1 U_1 + C_2 U_2 + \cdots + C_n U_n + Z_x \tag{11}$$

is a complete solution of (8).

We call (10) the *complementary function* and Z_x the *particular integral*. Consequently, the complete solution of (8) is the sum of the complementary function and the particular integral.

The linear equation with variable coefficients can be solved only under rather severe restrictions upon the coefficients. Even a general solution of the linear equation of second order with variable coefficients

$$U_{x+2} + p_1 U_{x+1} + p_2 U_x = r_x$$

has not been found. However, the general linear equation with *constant coefficients* is solvable and we now turn to its solution.

7. LINEAR EQUATIONS WITH CONSTANT COEFFICIENTS

The type of the equations which we shall consider in this section is of the form

$$U_{x+n} + A_1 U_{x+n-1} + \cdots + A_n U_x = X \qquad (12)$$

when $A_1, A_2, \cdots, A_n$ are constants and X is a function of x. It may be written in the symbolic form

$$(E^n + A_1 E^{n-1} + \cdots + A_n) U_x = X \qquad (13)$$

or, in short,

$$f(E) U_x = X \qquad (14)$$

where $f(E)$ is the rational integral function of E,

$$f(E) = E^n + A_1 E^{n-1} + \cdots + A_n$$

When the right-hand member of (12) or (13) is zero, the equation is said to be *homogeneous*. To find the solution of the homogeneous equation with constant coefficients,

$$U_{x+n} + A_1 U_{x+n-1} + \cdots + A_n U_x = 0 \qquad (15)$$

or

$$f(E) U_x = 0$$

we let

$$U_x = a^x, \quad a \neq 0$$

and find the values of a for which (15) is satisfied. Substituting in (15), we have

$$a^{x+n} + A_1 a^{x+n-1} + \cdots + A_n a^x = 0$$

or

$$a^x(a^n + A_1 a^{n-1} + \cdots + A^n) = 0$$

Therefore, if a^x is a solution of (15), it is necessary that

$$a^n + A_1 a^{n-1} + \cdots + A_n = 0 \qquad (16)$$

since a^x is not zero for any finite value of x.

Conversely, if a_1, a_2, $\cdots$, a_n are n distinct solutions of (16), then a_1^x, a_2^x, $\cdots$, a_n^x are solutions of (15) as can be proved by trial. Further,

$$U_x = C_1 a_1^x + C_2 a_2^x + \cdots + C_n a_n^x \qquad (17)$$

is a solution of (15).

Equation (16) is called the *auxiliary equation*[2] of (15), and (17) is the *general solution* of (15).

Therefore to solve the homogeneous equation with constant coefficients we solve the auxiliary equation for a. It has n solutions. If they are distinct, say a_1, a_2, $\cdots$, a_n, then (17) is the solution of (15).

Example 1. Find the solution of

$$U_{x+2} - 5U_{x+1} + 6U_x = 0$$

Solution: The auxiliary equation is

$$a^2 - 5a + 6 = 0$$

from which

$$a = 3, \quad a = 2$$

and the general solution is

$$U_x = C_1 2^x + C_2 3^x$$

The expressions 2^x, 3^x, $C_1 2^x$, and $C_2 3^x$ are particular solutions of the given equation.

It may happen that the auxiliary equation (16) may have multiple roots. In this case (17) is not the general solution, for it will not contain n arbitrary constants. If $a_1 = a_2$, then a_1^x and $x a_1^x$ are particular solutions of (15) and $(C_1 + C_2 x)a_1^x$ is the part of the general solution corresponding to this pair of equal roots. Similarly, it may be shown[3] that if k roots are equal, $a_1 = a_2 = a_3 = \cdots = a_k$, the general solution of (15) is

$$U_x = (C_1 + C_2 x + \cdots + C_k x^{k-1})a_k^x + C_{k+1}a^x_{k+1} + \cdots + C_n a_n^x$$

Example 2. Solve the equation

$$U_{x+3} - 3U_{x+1} - 2U_x = 0$$

---

[2] Called the *characteristic equation* by some writers.
[3] See Sections 10 and 11 of this chapter.

Solution: The auxiliary equation is

$$a^3 - 3a - 2 = 0$$

or

$$(a + 1)^2(a - 2) = 0, \quad a = -1, -1, 2$$

and the solution is

$$U_x = (C_1 + C_2 x)(-1)^x + C_3 2^x$$

If the coefficients of the difference equation are real, while some or all of the roots of the auxiliary equation are not, we can, by employing DeMoivre's Theorem,[4] transform our solution to contain only real terms. Thus, if the auxiliary equation has a root $A + iB$, it will also have the root $A - iB$ since its coefficients are real. The corresponding two terms of the solution will be

$$c_1(A + iB)^x + c_2(A - iB)^x$$

It is customary to convert this expression into functions of a real variable by changing the complex numbers to trigonometric form. Thus

$$c_1(A + iB)^x = c_1 r^x(\cos x\theta + i \sin x\theta)$$

and

$$c_2(A - iB)^x = c_2 r^x(\cos x\theta - i \sin x\theta)$$

Adding

$$c_1(A + iB)^x + c_2(a - iB)^x = r^x(C_1 \cos x\theta + C_2 \sin x\theta)$$

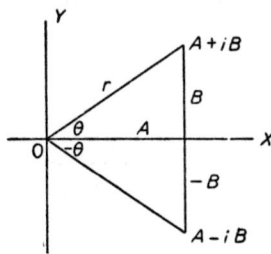

where $C_1 = c_1 + c_2$, $C_2 = i(c_1 - c_2)$.

$$r = +\sqrt{A^2 + B^2} \quad \text{and} \quad \theta = \text{arc tan}\, \frac{B}{A}$$

We shall leave it as an exercise for the student to show that, in case a pair of such roots is repeated, the corresponding part of the solution is

$$r^x[(C_1 + C_2 x) \cos x\theta + (C_3 + C_4 x) \sin x\theta]$$

[4] DeMoivre's Theorem: $(\cos \theta + i \sin \theta)^n = \cos n\theta + i \sin n\theta$.

Example 3. Solve $U_{x+2} + U_{x+1} + U_x = 0$.

Solution:

$$a^2 + a + 1 = 0$$

$$a = \frac{-1}{2} + \frac{i\sqrt{3}}{2}, \frac{-1}{2} - \frac{i\sqrt{3}}{2}$$

$$A = -\frac{1}{2}, \quad B = \frac{\sqrt{3}}{2}$$

$$r = \sqrt{A^2 + B^2} = 1, \quad \theta = \arctan(-\sqrt{3}) = \frac{2\pi}{3}$$

$$U_x = C_1 \cos \frac{2\pi}{3} x + C_2 \sin \frac{2\pi}{3} x$$

Exercises

Solve the equations:

1. $(E^3 + E^2 - 9E - 9)U_x = 0$.
2. $(E^2 - 7E + 6)U_x = 0$.
3. $U_{x+2} - 6U_{x+1} + 9U_x = 0$.
4. $U_{x+2} + 2U_{x+1} + 4U_x = 0$.
5. $(E^2 + E + 1)^2 U_x = 0$.
6. $U_{x+2} - 4U_x = 0$.
7. $U_{x+2} + 8U_{x+1} + 4U_x = 0$.
8. $U_{x+4} + U_x = 0$.

We have thus obtained a solution of the homogeneous linear equation,

$$U_{x+n} + A_1 U_{x+n-1} + \cdots + A_n U_x = 0$$

or

$$f(E)U_x = 0$$

We shall now proceed to the more general equation (14)

$$U_{x+n} + A_1 U_{x+n-1} + \cdots + A_n U_x = X$$

or

$$f(E)U_x = X \tag{14}$$

For convenience of language, the solution of (14), when the right-hand member is made zero temporarily, is called the *complementary function*. If now a particular integral of (14) can be found (no matter by what means), then the sum of the complementary function and the particular integral will constitute the general solution of (14). That is,

$$\frac{\text{General}}{\text{Solution}} = \frac{\text{Complementary}}{\text{Function}} + \frac{\text{Particular}}{\text{Integral}}$$

The complementary function is an expression that contains arbitrary constants equal in number to the order of the equation and causes $f(E)U_x$

to vanish. The particular integral is an expression that satisfies (14), and yet is not contained in the complementary function. Thus the sum of the C.F. and the P.I. is the general solution of (14).

Our task now is therefore reduced to finding a particular integral of (14). We shall employ two methods to find particular integrals: (a) the method of operators, and (b) the method of undetermined coefficients. The method of operators will require a few theorems that we shall now establish.

8. Some Helpful Theorems

Theorem I. If $f(E)$ is a polynomial in E, then

$$f(E)a^x = a^x f(a)$$

Proof. Let $f(E) = c_0 + c_1 E + c_2 E^2 + \cdots + c_n E^n$. Then

$$\begin{aligned}
f(E)a^x &= (c_0 + c_1 E + c_2 E^2 + \cdots + c_n E^n)a^x \\
&= c_0 a^x + c_1 a^{x+1} + c_2 a^{x+2} + \cdots + c_n a^{x+n} \\
&= a^x(c_0 + c_1 a + c_2 a^2 + \cdots + c_n a^n) \\
&= a^x f(a)
\end{aligned}$$

Theorem II. If $f(E)$ is a polynomial in E, and $F(x)$ is a function of x, then

Proof.
$$f(E)a^x F(x) = a^x f(aE)F(x)$$

$$\begin{aligned}
f(E)a^x F(x) &= (c_0 + c_1 E + c_2 E^2 + \cdots + c_n E^n)a^x F(x) \\
&= c_0 a^x F(x) + c_1 a^{x+1}F(x+1) + \cdots + c_n a^{x+n}F(x+n) \\
&= a^x[c_0 F(x) + c_1 a F(x+1) + \cdots + c_n a^n F(x+n)] \\
&= a^x[c_0 F(x) + c_1 a E F(x) + \cdots + c_n a^n E^n F(x)] \\
&= a^x[c_0 + c_1(aE) + \cdots + c_n(aE)^n]F(x) \\
&= a^x f(aE)F(x)
\end{aligned}$$

Theorem III. As a corollary to Theorem II we have

$$\begin{aligned}
(E - a)^n a^x F(x) &= a^x a^n (E - 1)^n F(x) \\
&= a^x a^n \Delta^n F(x)
\end{aligned}$$

Proof.
$$\begin{aligned}
(E - a)^n a^x F(x) &= a^x(aE - a)^n F(x) \\
&= a^x a^n (E - 1)^n F(x) \\
&= a^x a^n \Delta^n F(x)
\end{aligned}$$

since $E - 1 \equiv \Delta$.

We have written our general linear difference equation with constant co-efficients in the form

$$f(E)U_x = X$$

The particular integral to this equation is

$$U_x = \frac{1}{f(E)} X$$

where we define the right-hand member to be the expression which, when operated upon by $f(E)$, produces X.

Theorem IV.

$$\frac{1}{(E-a)^n} a^x = \frac{x^{(n)} a^{x-n}}{n!}$$

Proof. The proof of this theorem is established by induction.

$$\frac{1}{E-a} a^x = xa^{x-1} = \frac{x^{(1)}}{1!} a^{x-1}$$

since $(E-a)xa^{x-1} = (x+1)a^x - xa^x = a^x$. Hence the theorem is true for $n = 1$.

We now prove that if the theorem is true for $n = k$, it is true for $n = k + 1$. We have

$$\frac{1}{(E-a)^k} a^x = \frac{x^{(k)} a^{x-k}}{k!}$$

Then

$$\frac{1}{(E-a)^{k+1}} a^x = \frac{1}{(E-a)} \cdot \frac{1}{(E-a)^k} a^x = \frac{1}{E-a} \frac{x^{(k)} a^{x-k}}{k!}$$

Let

$$\frac{1}{(E-a)} \frac{x^{(k)} a^{x-k}}{k!} = a^x V_x$$

Operating on both members by $(E-a)$

$$(E-a)a^x V_x = \frac{x^{(k)}}{k!} a^{x-k}$$

or

$$a^{x+1}(V_{x+1} - V_x) = \frac{x^{(k)} a^{x-k}}{k!}$$

$$\Delta V_x = \frac{x^{(k)}}{k!} a^{-(k+1)}$$

$$V_x = \frac{x^{(k+1)}}{(k+1)!} a^{-(k+1)}$$

Hence,

$$\frac{1}{(E-a)^{k+1}} a^x = a^x V_x = \frac{x^{(k+1)}}{(k+1)!} a^{x-(k+1)}$$

Therefore, if the theorem is true for $n = k$, it is true for $n = k+1$. By counting, it is true for $n = n$.

As a consequence of Theorem I we have Theorem V.

Theorem V.

$$\frac{1}{f(E)} a^x = \frac{1}{f(a)} \cdot a^x, \quad f(a) \neq 0$$

Proof. We let

$$\frac{1}{f(E)} a^x = V_x$$

where V_x is to be determined.

Operating by $f(E)$ we have

$$f(E) V_x = a^x$$

But by Theorem I

$$f(E) \frac{a^x}{f(a)} = a^x, \quad f(a) \neq 0$$

Hence,

$$f(E) V_x = f(E) \frac{a^x}{f(a)}$$

and thus

$$V_x = \frac{a^x}{f(a)}$$

or

$$\frac{1}{f(E)} a^x = \frac{a^x}{f(a)}, \quad f(a) \neq 0$$

Theorem VI. If $F(x)$ is a polynomial in x

$$\frac{1}{f(E)} a^x F(x) = a^x \frac{1}{f(aE)} F(x), \quad f(aE) \neq 0$$

Proof of this theorem is left as an exercise for the student.

Theorem VII. If $f(\Delta)$ is a polynomial in Δ, then $f(\Delta) a^x = a^x f(a-1)$.

Proof.

$$f(\Delta)a^x = (c_0 + c_1\Delta + c_2\Delta^2 + \cdots + c_n\Delta^n)a^x$$
$$= c_0a^x + c_1a^x(a-1) + c_2a^x(a-1)^2 + \cdots + c_na^x(a-1)^n$$
$$= a^x[c_0 + c_1(a-1) + c_2(a-1)^2 + \cdots + c_n(a-1)^n]$$
$$= a^xf(a-1)$$

From Theorem VII we have immediately Theorem VIII.

Theorem VIII.

$$\frac{1}{f(\Delta)}a^x = \frac{a^x}{f(a-1)}, \quad f(a-1) \neq 0$$

where $f(\Delta) \cdot \dfrac{1}{f(\Delta)}X = X$ defines $\dfrac{1}{f(\Delta)}X$.

9. Applications of Theorems. Illustrative Examples

Example 1. Solve the equation

$$U_{x+2} - 5U_{x+1} + 6U_x = 5^x$$

Solution: The auxiliary equation is

$$a^2 - 5a + 6 = 0$$

$$a = 3, 2$$

The complementary function is

$$\text{C.F.} = C_1 3^x + C_2 2^x$$

By the method of operators the particular integral is

$$\text{P.I.} = \frac{1}{E^2 - 5E + 6}5^x = \frac{1}{5^2 - 5 \cdot 5 + 6}5^x = \frac{5^x}{6}$$

The complete solution is

$$U_x = \text{C.F.} + \text{P.I.} = C_1 3^x + C_2 2^x + \frac{5^x}{6}$$

The P.I. can also be found by undetermined coefficients. Let $U_x = a \cdot 5^x$. Then

$$a5^{x+2} - 5a5^{x+1} + 6a5^x = 5^x$$

$$5^x(25a - 25a + 6a) = 5^x$$

$$6a = 1$$

$$a = \tfrac{1}{6}$$

Therefore the P.I. is $5^x/6$ as before.

Example 2. Solve $(E^2 - 5E + 6)U_x = 3^x$.

Solution: As in Example I,

$$\text{C.F.} = C_1 3^x + C_2 2^x$$

$$\text{P.I.} = \frac{1}{E - 3} \cdot \frac{1}{E - 2} 3^x = \frac{1}{E - 3} 3^x = x3^{x-1}$$

applying Theorems V and IV, successively. The complete solution, C.S., is

$$\text{C.S.} = U_x = C_1 3^x + C_2 2^x + x3^{x-1}$$

Since 3 is a root of the auxiliary equation

$$a^2 - 5a + 6 = 0$$

to find the P.I. by undetermined coefficients we let $U_x = ax3^x$. Then

$$(E^2 - 5E + 6)ax3^x = 3^x$$

$$a(x + 2)3^{x+2} - 5a(x + 1)3^{x+1} + 6ax3^x = 3^x$$

$$9a(x + 2) - 15a(x + 1) + 6ax = 1$$

$$3a = 1$$

$$a = \tfrac{1}{3}$$

and P.I. $= x3^x/3 = x3^{x-1}$ as before.

Example 3. Solve $U_{x+2} + U_{x+1} + U_x = x^2 + x + 1$.

Solution: The auxiliary equation is

$$a^2 + a + 1 = 0$$

$$a = -\frac{1}{2} + i\frac{\sqrt{3}}{2}, \quad a = -\frac{1}{2} - i\frac{\sqrt{3}}{2}$$

$$A = -\frac{1}{2}, \quad B = \frac{\sqrt{3}}{2}, \quad r = 1, \quad \theta = \frac{2\pi}{3}$$

$$\text{C.F.} = C_1 \cos\frac{2\pi x}{3} + C_2 \sin\frac{2\pi x}{3}$$

In the Δ form the given equation can be written

$$(3 + 3\Delta + \Delta^2)U_x = x^2 + x + 1$$

and the

$$\text{P.I.} = \frac{1}{3 + 3\Delta + \Delta^2}(x^2 + x + 1)$$

Writing $\dfrac{1}{3 + 3\Delta + \Delta^2}$ in a series in ascending powers of Δ we find

$$\text{P.I.} = \tfrac{1}{3}[1 - \Delta + \tfrac{2}{3}\Delta^2 - \cdots](x^2 + x + 1)$$

$$= \tfrac{1}{3}[1 - \Delta + \tfrac{2}{3}\Delta^2 - \cdots](x^{(2)} + 2x + 1)$$

$$= \frac{1}{3}\left[x^{(2)} + \frac{1}{3}\right] = \frac{x^2}{3} - \frac{x}{3} + \frac{1}{9}$$

$$\text{C.S.} = \text{C.F.} + \text{P.I.}$$

The P.I. may also be found by undetermined coefficients. Let $U_x = ax^2 + bx + c$. We leave it as an exercise for the student to show that $a = \tfrac{1}{3}$, $b = -\tfrac{1}{3}$, $c = \tfrac{1}{9}$.

Example 4.　Solve $U_{x+2} - 7U_{x+1} - 8U_x = x^{(2)}2^x$.

Solution: The auxiliary equation is

$$a^2 - 7a - 8 = 0$$

$$a = -1, 8$$

$$\text{C.F.} = C_1(-1)^x + C_2'(8)^x$$

To find the P.I. we let $U_x = 2^x V_x$.　Our equation then reduces to

$$4V_{x+2} - 14V_{x+1} - 8V_x = x^{(2)}$$

$$(4E^2 - 14E - 8)V_x = x^{(2)}$$

$$V_x = \frac{1}{-8 - 14E + 4E^2}x^{(2)}$$

$$= \frac{1}{-18 - 6\Delta + 4\Delta^2}x^{(2)} \text{ since } E \equiv 1 + \Delta$$

$$= \left(-\frac{1}{18} + \frac{1}{54}\Delta - \frac{1}{54}\Delta^2 - \cdots\right)x^{(2)}$$

$$V_x = -\frac{1}{54}[3x^2 - 5x + 2]$$

$$\text{P.I.} = 2^x V_x = \frac{-2^x}{54}[3x^2 - 5x + 2]$$

$$\text{C.S.} = \text{C.F.} + \text{P.I.}$$

We can also find the P.I. by employing Theorem VI of the preceding section:

$$\frac{1}{f(E)}a^x F(x) = a^x \frac{1}{f(aE)}F(x)$$

We have $F(x) = x^{(2)}$, $a = 2$, and $f(E) = E^2 - 7E - 8$ since $U_{x+2} - 7U_{x+1} - 8U_x = (E^2 - 7E - 8)U_x$.

$$\text{P.I.} = \frac{1}{E^2 - 7E - 8}2^x x^{(2)} = 2^x \frac{1}{-8 - 14E + 4E^2}x^{(2)}$$

which can be completed as before.

Of course we can employ undetermined coefficients to determine the P.I. To do this we let $U_x = (ax^{(2)} + bx^{(1)} + c)2^x$.

Example 5. Given the equation $f(E)U_x = a^x F(x)$ where $F(x)$ is a function of x. Show that the substitution $U_x = a^x V_x$ leads to the determination of V_x, namely,

$$V_x = \frac{1}{f(aE)}F(x), \quad f(aE) \neq 0$$

Proof. Employing the given substitution

$$f(E)a^x V_x = a^x F(x)$$

$$a^x f(aE)V_x = a^x F(x)$$

$$V_x = \frac{1}{f(aE)}F(x)$$

10. SELIWANOFF'S TREATMENT OF THE HOMOGENEOUS LINEAR EQUATION WITH CONSTANT COEFFICIENTS [5]

Consider the homogeneous linear equation

$$U_{x+n} + A_1 U_{x+n-1} + A_2 U_{x+n-2} + \cdots + A_n U_x = 0 \tag{18}$$

Let

$$U_x = a^x V_x \tag{19}$$

where V_x is a polynomial of mth degree.

[5] Seliwanoff, D., *Lehrbuch der Differenzenrechnung*, p. 77.

Replacing U_{x+i}, $i = 1, 2, \cdots, n$, by the values

$$U_{x+1} = a^{x+1}V_{x+1} = a^{x+1}[V_x + \Delta V_x]$$

$$U_{x+2} = a^{x+2}V_{x+2} = a^{x+2}[V_x + 2\Delta V_x + \Delta^2 V_x]$$

$$U_{x+3} = a^{x+3}V_{x+3} = a^{x+3}[V_x + 3\Delta V_x + 3\Delta^2 V_x + \Delta^3 V_x]$$

$$\cdot \quad \cdot \quad \cdot \quad \cdot \quad \cdot \quad \cdot \quad \cdot \quad \cdot \quad \cdot \quad \cdot \quad \cdot \quad \cdot \quad \cdot \quad \cdot \quad \cdot \quad \cdot \quad \cdot \quad \cdot \quad \cdot$$

$$U_{x+n} = a^{x+n}\left[V_x + n\Delta V_x + \frac{n^{(2)}}{2!}\Delta^2 V_x + \cdots + \Delta^n V_x\right]$$

equation (18) becomes

$$a^x[a^n + A_1 a^{n-1} + A_2 a^{n-2} + \cdots + A_n]V_x$$

$$+ a^{x+1}[na^{n-1} + (n-1)A_1 a^{n-2} + (n-2)A_2 a^{n-3} + \cdots + A_{n-1}]\Delta V_x$$

$$+ a^{x+2}[n(n-1)a^{n-2} + (n-1)(n-2)A_1 a^{n-3} + \cdots + 2A_{n-2}]\frac{\Delta^2 V_x}{1 \cdot 2}$$

$$+ \cdots + a^{x+n}n!\frac{\Delta^n V_x}{n!} = 0$$

or, in brief, equation (18) under the substitution (19) becomes

$$a^x f(a)V_x + a^{x+1}f'(a)\Delta V_x + a^{x+2}f''(a)\frac{\Delta^2 V_x}{2!}$$

$$+ \cdots + a^{x+n}f^{(n)}(a)\frac{\Delta^n V_x}{n!} = 0 \quad (20)$$

where $f(a)$ is the auxiliary function

$$f(a) \equiv a^n + A_1 a^{n-1} + \cdots + A_n$$

If $a = a_1$ is a simple root of $f(a) = 0$, and $V_x = 1$, then equation (20) is satisfied and $(a_1)^x$ is a particular solution of (18). If $a_1, a_2, a_3, \cdots, a_n$ are n simple roots of $f(a) = 0$, particular solutions of (18) are $(a_1)^x$, $(a_2)^x$, $\cdots$, $(a_n)^x$, and the general solution is

$$U_x = C_1(a_1)^x + C_2(a_2)^x + C_3(a_3)^x + \cdots + C_n(a_n)^x$$

If a_1 is a k-fold root,[6] of $f(a) = 0$, $a_1 = a_2 = a_3 = \cdots = a_k = a$, $f(a) = f'(a) = f''(a) = \cdots = f^{(k-1)}(a) = 0$, and equation (20) reduces to

[6] Dickson, L. E., *First Course in the Theory of Equations*, p. 61.

$$a^{x+k}f^{(k)}(a)\frac{\Delta^k V_x}{k!} + a^{x+k+1}f^{(k+1)}(a)\frac{\Delta^{k+1} V_x}{(k+1)!}$$

$$+\cdots+ a^{x+n}f^{(n)}(a)\frac{\Delta^n V_x}{n!} = 0$$

This equation is satisfied if V_x is a polynomial of degree $(k-1)$. Hence a particular solution of (18) is

$$U_x = (C_1 + C_2 x + C_3 x^2 + \cdots + C_k x^{k-1})a_k{}^x$$

Assuming all other roots are real and distinct, the general solution of (18) is

$$U_x = (C_1 + C_2 x + C_3 x^2 + \cdots + C_k x^{k-1})a_k{}^x + C_{k+1}a^x{}_{k+1} + \cdots + C_n a_n{}^x$$

11. Multiple Roots in Auxiliary Equation by Operators

Consider the question

$$U_{x+2} - 4U_{x+1} + 4U_x = 0 \tag{21}$$

or

$$(E - 2)^2 U_x = 0$$

The auxiliary equation

$$a^2 - 4a + 4 = 0$$

has the equal roots $a_1 = a_2 = 2$.

Let

$$U_x = 2^x V_x$$

then (21) becomes

$$2^{x+2}(V_{x+2} - 2V_{x+1} + V_x) = 0$$

or

$$2^{x+2}\Delta^2 V_x = 0$$

from which

$$\Delta^2 V_x = 0$$

$$V_x = C_1 + C_2 x$$

and

$$U_x = (C_1 + C_2 x)2^x$$

In a similar manner consider the equation

$$(E - a_k)^k U_x = 0 \tag{22}$$

The auxiliary equation

$$(a - a_k)^k = 0$$

has k equal roots $a_1 = a_2 = \cdots = a_k$.

Let
$$U_x = a_k{}^x V_x$$

then (22) becomes

$$a_k{}^{x+k}\Delta^k V_x = 0$$

from which

$$\Delta^k V_x = 0$$

$$V_x = C_1 + C_2 x + C_3 x^2 + \cdots + C_k x^{k-1}$$

and

$$U_x = (C_1 + C_2 x + \cdots + C_k x^{k-1})a_k{}^x$$

Finally, if the given equation

$$f(E)U_x = 0 \qquad (23)$$

has the auxiliary equation

$$(a - a_1)^a (a - a_2)^b \cdots (a - a_k)^k = 0 \qquad (24)$$

where $a_1, a_2, \cdots, a_k$ are distinct, then a_1 is of multiplicity a; a_2 is of multiplicity b, and so on, and $a + b + \cdots + k = n$. In this case (23) can be written symbolically

$$(E - a_1)^a (E - a_2)^b \cdots (E - a_k)^k U_x = 0 \qquad (25)$$

The order in which the factors in (25) are written is immaterial since $f(E)$ enjoys the commutative property.

Choosing U_x to satisfy

$$(E - a_k)^k U_x = 0$$

we then have a solution of the given equation (22)

$$U_x = (C_1 + C_2 x + \cdots + C_k x^{k-1})a_k{}^x$$

Treating each factor of (25) in the same way we arrive at the several particular solutions of (25). The general solution is their sum

$$U_x = (A_1 + A_2 x + \cdots + A_a x^{a-1})a_1{}^x + (B_1 + B_2 x + \cdots + B_b x^{b-1})a_2{}^x$$

$$+ \cdots + (C_1 + C_2 x + \cdots + C_k x^{k-1})a_k{}^x$$

Thus, for example, if we have

$$(E - 2)^3 (E + 3)^2 U_x = 0$$

the solution is

$$U_x = (A_1 + A_2 x + A_3 x^2)2^x + (B_1 + B_2 x)(-3)^x$$

12. SIMULTANEOUS EQUATIONS

Instead of a single equation involving one function, we may encounter a system of n equations involving n unknown functions. Of course the solution is obtained by elimination in such a way as to obtain an equation involving only one of the functions. Solving it for the unknown, by substitution or otherwise, we may be able to obtain the other unknown functions. Consider the system

$$U_{x+1} - V_x = 0$$
$$V_{x+1} - U_x = 0$$

From the first

$$U_{x+2} - V_{x+1} = 0$$

Substituting from the second we obtain

$$U_{x+2} - U_x = 0$$

$$U_x = C_1 + C_2(-1)^x.$$

Substituting this value in the second equation

$$V_{x+1} = C_1 + C_2(-1)^x$$
$$V_x = C_1 + C_2(-1)^{x-1} = C_1 - C_2(-1)^x$$

Exercises

Solve the following equations:

1. $U_{x+2} - 5U_{x+1} + 6U_x = 4^x$.
2. $U_{x+2} - 2U_{x+1} + U_x = 2^x + x^{(2)}$.
3. $U_{x+2} - 7U_{x+1} + 12U_x = x^{(3)} + x^{(2)}4^x + 4^x$.
4. $(\Delta^2 + 4\Delta + 4)U_x = x^3$.
5. $(\Delta^2 + \Delta)U_x = x + \sin x$.
6. $U_{x+2} + U_x = \cos x$.
7. If \$1 is deposited in a bank at an interest rate i, what is the amount at the end of x years?
8. A man's salary begins at \$a and increases annually in arithmetical progression with a common difference of \$b. If he saves $1/m$th of his income each year and invests it at rate i, what will be his income in the xth year?
9. In problems of reproduction in genetics we encounter the following problem. If $U_0 = 1$, $U_1 = 2$, and each succeeding term is the sum of the two preceding terms, find U_x [The *Fibonacci Series*].
10. Solve: $U_{n+2} - U_{n+1} + U_n = n^2$.
11. If $3U_{x+3} - 7U_{x+2} + 5U_{x+1} - U_x = 0$, and $U_1 = 1$, $U_2 = 8$, $U_3 = 17$, find
    (a) U_x and (b) $\sum_1^n U_x$.

12. The first term of a sequence is 1, and every other term is twice the preceding term. Find the nth term.

13. If $2U_{x+1} - U_x = (x + 1)a$, show that

$$U_x = \frac{U_0}{2^x} + a\left(x - 1 + \frac{1}{2^x}\right)$$

14. The first term of a sequence is a, the second term is b, and every other term is the arithmetic mean of the two preceding terms. Show that

$$U_x = \frac{a + 2b}{3} - \frac{a - b}{3}\left(-\frac{1}{2}\right)^{x-2}$$

15. Show that x straight lines, no two of which are parallel and no three of which meet in a point, divide a plane into

$$\frac{x}{2}(x + 1) + 1 \text{ parts}$$

16. There are p points in a plane, no three of which, except q, are in the same straight line. Find the number of straight lines and the number of triangles which result from joining them.

17. In a plane n circles are drawn so that each circle intersects all the others, and no three meet in a point. Prove that the plane is divided into $(n^2 - n + 2)$ parts.

18. Obtain a particular solution of $U_{x+2} - 5U_{x+1} + 6U_x = x + 2$ by assuming $U_x = ax + b$ and equating coefficients. Then find the general solution of the equation.

19. Find the general solution of $U_{x+2} - 5U_{x+1} + 6U_x = 7^x$. Assume $U_x = a \cdot 7^x$ as a trial solution.

A difference equation may be reduced to an integrable form by making a suitable substitution. As an illustration, consider

$$U_{x+1} - 2U_x^2 + 1 = 0$$

Let

$$U_x = \cos V_x$$

Then

$$\cos V_{x+1} = 2\cos^2 V_x - 1 = \cos 2V_x$$

$$V_{x+1} - 2V_x = 0$$

$$V_x = C\prod_0^{x-1} 2 = C \cdot 2^x$$

Hence,

$$U_x = \cos(C \cdot 2^x)$$

20. Solve the equation $U_{x+1}U_x + aU_x + b = 0$.

Hint: Let $U_x = 1/V_x + m$, where m is a root of $m^2 + ma + b = 0$. The reduced equation is $(m + a)V_{x+1} + mV_x + 1 = 0$.

21. Solve: $U_{x+1}U_x + (x + 2)U_{x+1} + xU_x + x^2 + 2x + 2 = 0$.

Let $U_x = V_{x+1}/V_x - (x + 2)$ and the reduced equation becomes

$$V_{x+2} - 3V_{x+1} + 2V_x = 0$$

22. Show that the general solution of the equation

$$U_{x+1}U_x + aU_{x+1} + bU_x + c = 0$$

can be written in the form

$$U_x = \frac{A\alpha^{x+1} + \beta^{x+1}}{A\alpha^x + \beta^x} - a$$

where A is an arbitrary constant and α and β are roots of the equation

$$x^2 - (a - b)x + c - ab = 0$$

and

$$(a + b)^2 \neq 4c$$

Hint: Let $U_x + a = V_{x+1}/V_x$, and thus obtain the equation

$$V_{x+2} + (b - a)V_{x+1} + (c - ab)V_x = 0$$

23. Show that in No. 22 above if $(a + b)^2 = 4c$, then

$$U_x = \frac{a - b}{2(A + x)} - \frac{a + b}{2}$$

24. Solve: $U_{x+1}U_x + 3U_{x+1} - 4U_x - 2 = 0$.
25. Solve: $U_{x+1}U_x + 5U_{x+1} + U_x + 9 = 0$.
26. If $(2x - U_x)U_{x+1} = x(x + 1)$ and $U_1 = a$, show that

$$U_x = x\left[\frac{2a + x - ax - 1}{a + x - ax}\right]$$

Hint: Let $U_x = xV_x$.

27. Solve: $U_{x+1} - V_x = 2^x$
$\qquad\quad V_{x+1} - U_x = 0$

28. Solve: $U_{x+1} - V_x = 2x$
$\qquad\quad V_{x+1} - U_x = -2x$

29. Solve: $\left.\begin{array}{l}U_{x+1} + 2V_{x+1} - U_x = 0 \\ V_{x+1} - 2U_x - V_x = a^x\end{array}\right\}$ or $\left\{\begin{array}{l}(E - 1)U_x + 2EV_x = 0 \\ -2U_x + (E - 1)V_x = a^x\end{array}\right.$

Hint: Multiply the first equation by 2, operate upon the second by $(E - 1)$, and add the results.

30. Show that $(x - 2)!$ is a P.I. of the equation

$$U_{x+2} - 3xU_{x+1} + 2x(x - 1)U_x = 0$$

Employ the substitution $U_x = (x - 2)!V_x$ and thus solve the given equation.

13. Rational Fractions.   The Psi Function [7]

The reader may have noted that in our discussion of finite integration and finite summation in Chapter II nothing was said regarding such prob-

---

[7] The psi function is sometimes called the digamma function $F(x)$. They are connected by the relation $\psi(x) = F(x - 1)$.

lems as $\Delta^{-1} \dfrac{a}{(x-b)^n}$ and $\Delta^{-1} \log x$. The use of partial fractions, so power-ful in the infinitesimal calculus, has been studiously avoided. If a question were raised about finding $\sum\limits_{1}^{n} \dfrac{1}{x}$, we should be compelled to state that the summation cannot be effected in terms of the elementary functions. We now turn our attention to finding $\Delta^{-1} \dfrac{a}{(x-b)^n}$.

From the equation

$$\Gamma(x+1) = x\Gamma(x) \tag{26}$$

we obtain by logarithmic differentiation

$$\frac{\Gamma'(x+1)}{\Gamma(x+1)} = \frac{1}{x} + \frac{\Gamma'(x)}{\Gamma(x)} \tag{27}$$

Denoting

$$\frac{\Gamma'(x)}{\Gamma(x)} \equiv \frac{d}{dx} \log \Gamma(x)$$

by $\psi(x)$, equation (27) may be written

$$\psi(x+1) = \frac{1}{x} + \psi(x) \tag{28}$$

$$\Delta\psi(x) = \frac{1}{x}$$

and

$$\Delta^{-1} \frac{1}{x} = \psi(x)$$

We are now able to find $\sum\limits_{1}^{n} \dfrac{1}{x}$. Thus,

$$\sum_{1}^{n} \frac{1}{x} = \Delta^{-1} \frac{1}{x} \bigg]_{1}^{n+1} = \psi(n+1) - \psi(1)$$

which can be evaluated from tables [8] of the psi function.

Differentiating equation (28) we have

$$\psi'(x+1) = -\frac{1}{x^2} + \psi'(x) \tag{29}$$

---

[8] See Pairman, *Tables of the Digamma and Trigamma Functions*. Cambridge University Press, 1919.

that is,

$$\Delta\psi'(x) = -\frac{1}{x^2}$$

or

$$\Delta^{-1}\left(-\frac{1}{x^2}\right) = \psi'(x)$$

Similarly, by repeated differentiation we obtain

$$\psi^{(m)}(x) = \Delta^{-1}\frac{(-1)^m m!}{x^{m+1}} \tag{30}$$

from which it follows that

$$\Delta^{-1}\frac{1}{(x-b)^m} = \frac{(-1)^{1-m}}{(m-1)!}\psi^{(m-1)}(x-b) \tag{31}$$

With the aid of this result we are now in a position to sum any rational function.

From the equation defining $\psi(x)$ we have

$$\psi(x)\,dx = d\log\Gamma(x)$$

and thus

$$\int_x^{x+1}\psi(x)\,dx = \log\Gamma(x+1) - \log\Gamma(x) = \log x$$

Furthermore, it is evident that $U_x = \log\Gamma(x)$ is a solution of the equation

$$U_{x+1} - U_x = \log x$$

That is,

$$\Delta\log\Gamma(x) = \log x$$

or

$$\Delta^{-1}\log x = \log\Gamma(x)$$

This property makes possible the solution of the problem $\sum_1^n \log x$ for

$$\sum_1^n \log x = \Delta^{-1}\log x]_1^{n+1} = \log\Gamma(x)]_1^{n+1} = \log\Gamma(n+1)$$

Exercises

1. Find $\Delta^{-1}\dfrac{1}{x(x+3)}$ by two methods.

2. Find $\Delta^{-1}\dfrac{1}{(x-1)(2x-1)(5x-2)}$.

3. Solve: $\Delta U_x = \ln[a(x+b)^n]$.

4. Solve: $\ln 3U_{x+1} - \ln xU_x = 2$.

14. Miscellaneous Equations

In our consideration of linear equations we have been able to solve with completeness the equation of the first order

$$p_x U_{x+1} + q_x U_x = r_x$$

We have been able to solve with completeness the linear equation of order n with constant coefficients. Equations with functional coefficients are generally not solvable as closed expressions. Truly, a great deal is known about the properties of such equations, but to find their solutions generally presents an impossible problem. Certain special forms, however, may be solved by certain artifices.

Consider, for example, the equation

$$p_x U_x U_{x+1} + q_x U_{x+1} + r_x U_x = 0$$

when p_x, q_x, r_x are functions of x. Dividing by $U_x U_{x+1}$ we obtain

$$\frac{r_x}{U_{x+1}} + \frac{q_x}{U_x} + p_x = 0$$

It is obvious now that if we use the substitution

$$V_x = \frac{1}{U_x}$$

we will obtain a linear equation of the first order

$$r_x V_{x+1} + q_x V_x + p_x = 0$$

which is of course solvable.

The equation

$$U_{x+1} U_x - A_x(U_{x+1} - U_x) + 1 = 0$$

when placed in the form

$$\frac{U_{x+1} - U_x}{1 + U_{x+1} U_x} = \frac{1}{A_x}$$

suggests the substitution $U_x = \tan V_x$ which leads to

$$\tan \Delta V_x = 1/A_x$$

or to

$$\Delta V_x = \text{arc tan } 1/A_x$$

from which

$$U_x = \tan [\Delta^{-1} \text{ arc tan } 1/A_x + C]$$

An equation homogeneous in U_x, the general form of which is

$$f\left(\frac{U_{x+1}}{U_x}, x\right) = 0$$

can be reduced to a linear equation by the substitution $U_{x+1} = Z_x U_x$. Thus, consider

$$U^2_{x+1} - 5U_{x+1}U_x + 6U_x^2 = 0$$

Employing the suggested substitution we obtain

$$Z_x^2 - 5Z_x + 6 = 0$$

$$Z_x = 3, \text{ or } 2$$

$$U_{x+1} = 3U_x, \quad U_{x+1} = 2U_x$$

$$U_x = C3^x \quad \text{or} \quad U_x = C2^x$$

15. The Linear Equation of Order Two

Consider next the general linear difference equation of the second order

$$Z_{x+2} + A_x Z_{x+1} + B_x Z_x = C_x \tag{32}$$

where, as indicated, A_x, B_x, and C_x are functions of x. No method is yet known for solving equation (32) in terms of its coefficients. However, under certain restrictions solutions can be effected. Thus, if we by some means can find a P.I. of (32) when C_x is zero, or, in other words, if we can find a P.I. of the homogeneous equation obtained from (32) when C_x is replaced by zero, the order of the equation can be depressed by unity. For example, consider

$$Z_{x+2} - x(x+1)Z_x = 0$$

By trial it is found that $(x-1)!$ is a P.I. We let

$$Z_x = (x-1)!U_x$$

where U_x is to be determined. We find under the given substitution that

$$(x+1)![U_{x+2} - U_x] = 0$$

and hence

$$U_x = C_1 + C_2(-1)^x$$

and

$$Z_x = [C_1 + C_2(-1)^x](x-1)!$$

Let us now return to equation (32) where we apply the substitution $Z_x = U_x V_x$. Recalling that

$$Z_{x+1} = V_{x+1} U_{x+1} = V_{x+1}(U_x + \Delta U_x)$$

$$Z_{x+2} = V_{x+2} U_{x+2} = V_{x+2}(U_x + 2\Delta U_x + \Delta^2 U_x)$$

equation (32) becomes

$$V_{x+2}\Delta^2 U_x + (2V_{x+2} + A_x V_{x+1})\Delta U_x$$
$$+ (V_{x+2} + A_x V_{x+1} + B_x V_x)U_x = C_x \quad (33)$$

If V_x is a P.I. of (32) when $C_x = 0$, equation (33) becomes

$$\Delta^2 U_x + \frac{(2V_{x+2} + A_x V_{x+1})}{V_{x+2}}\,\Delta U_x = \frac{C_x}{V_{x+2}} \quad (34)$$

Now replacing ΔU_x by W_x, we have

$$W_{x+1} + P_x W_x = Q_x \quad (35)$$

where

$$P_x = 1 + \frac{A_x V_{x+1}}{V_{x+2}}, \quad Q_x = \frac{C_x}{V_{x+2}} \quad (36)$$

Since (35) is linear of the first order, which type is always solvable, equation (32) is solvable if a P.I. can be found for the homogeneous equation obtained from (32) when C_x is replaced by zero.

The value of this method depends upon our ability to discover particular integrals. The following suggestions may prove helpful:

(a) x is a P.I. of $\Delta^2 U_x + P_x \Delta U_x + Q_x U_x = 0$ if $P_x = -xQ_x$.
(b) A^x is a P.I. of $U_{x+2} + P_x U_{x+1} + Q_x U_x = 0$ if A is a root of $A^2 + P_x A + Q_x = 0$.
(c) $(x - a)!$ is often a P.I. of $U_{x+2} + P_x U_{x+1} + Q_x U_x = 0$ when P_x and Q_x are polynomials.

Exercises

1. Show that $\binom{n}{x}$ is a P.I. of $(x + 1)U_{x+1} - (n - x)U_x = 0$. Let $U_x = \binom{n}{x} V_x$ and solve the given equation.

2. Show that x is a P.I. of $U_{x+2} - \dfrac{2(x + 2)}{x + 1} U_{x+1} + \dfrac{x + 2}{x} U_x = 0$. Let $U_x = xV_x$ and solve the given equation.

3. Show that $U_x = a^{x^{(2)}/2}$ is a P.I. of

$$U_{x+2} - a(a^x + 1)U_{x+1} + a^{x+1}U_x = 0$$

and find the general solution.

4. In the theory of moments of beams we meet the equation

$$U_{x+2} + 4U_{x+1} + U_x = -\frac{ql^2}{2}$$

where q and l are constants.

Given $U_0 = U_n = 0$ and a_1 and a_2 are roots of $a^2 + 4a + 1 = 0$, show that the complete solution is

$$U_x = -\frac{ql^2}{12}\left[1 + \left(\frac{a_2{}^n - 1}{a_1{}^n - a_2{}^n}\right)a_1{}^x - \left(\frac{a_1{}^n - 1}{a_1{}^n - a_2{}^n}\right)a_2{}^x\right]$$

5. Show that $Z_x = x$ is a P.I. of

$$(x+1)^2 Z_{x+2} - (2x+1)(x+2)Z_{x+1} + (x+1)(x+2)Z_x = 0$$

Using the substitution $Z_x = xU_x$ followed by $\Delta U_x = W_x$ show that

$$(x+1)W_{x+1} - xW_x = 0$$

6. Show that $x!$ is a P.I. of

$$U_{x+2} - (x+1)(U_{x+1} + U_x) = 0$$

7. Show that 3^x is a P.I. of

$$U_{x+2} - x^{(2)}U_{x+1} + (3x^{(2)} - 9)U_x = 0$$

16. Concluding Remarks

As a final word in concluding this Introduction to Finite Differences, we wish to emphasize the fact that we have attempted to give a mere introduction into a broad field. There are many topics that we have not touched. There are many other topics that we have not explored deeply. For the student who is interested in a further study of this important field, when he shall have acquired a sufficient background he may venture into the following books:

Batchelder, P. M., *An Introduction to Linear Difference Equations.* Harvard Univ. Press.

Fort, Tomlinson, *Finite Differences.* Oxford University Press.

Jordan, Charles, *Calculus of Finite Differences.* Chelsea Publishing Company.

Markoff, A. A., *Differenzenrechnung.* B. G. Teubner, Leipzig.

Milne-Thompson, L. M., *The Calculus of Finite Differences.* Macmillan and Co., Limited.

Nörlund, N. E., *Differenzenrechnung.* Julius Springer, Berlin.

Seliwanoff, D., *Lehrbuch der Differenzenrechnung.* B. G. Teubner, Leipzig.

Appendix I

MATHEMATICAL INDUCTION

1. Introduction. *Mathematical induction* is the name applied to a powerful method of proving certain types of theorems and in establishing the validity of certain formulas in mathematics. It should be emphasized it is *not a method of discovery* but rather a method of *verification* of theorems or formulas that are believed, but not definitely known, to be true. The method can be used only with theorems or formulas that depend upon a variable which assumes only *positive integral values*.

2. Method of Mathematical Induction. In general, a proof by the method of mathematical induction requires three parts, namely:

Part I. Verification. This consists in showing that the proposition is true for some particular cases, usually for the smallest values of n for which the theorem is true. It is sufficient to verify the theorem for the very first case, but frequently we establish the validity of the proposition for the first few cases. It is for this reason that the word *induction* is used in the method.

Part II. Extension. The second part of the proof consists in proving the lemma: if the proposition is true for $n = k$, then it is true for $n = k + 1$. This usually constitutes the more difficult part of the proof.

Part III. Conclusion. This portion of the proof consists in combining I and II to prove the general theorem. (Of course, it is assumed that by continually adding 1 we can count to n.)

Example 1. If S_n is the sum of the first n terms of a geometrical progression:

$$S_n = a + ar + ar^2 + \cdots + ar^{n-1}$$

prove by mathematical induction that

$$S_n = \frac{a(1 - r^n)}{1 - r}, \quad r \neq 1$$

Proof.

Part I.   Letting $n = 1, 2, 3$ we have

$$S_1 = a = \frac{a(1 - r)}{1 - r}$$

$$S_2 = a + ar = \frac{a(1 - r^2)}{1 - r}$$

$$S_3 = a + ar + ar^2 = \frac{a(1 - r^3)}{1 - r}$$

Clearly the theorem is true for $n = 1, 2,$ and 3.

Part II.   Suppose for the sake of argument that the theorem is true for $n = k$. We show that *if* the theorem is true for $n = k$, then it is true for $n = k + 1$.   That is, if

$$S_k = a + ar + ar^2 + \cdots + ar^{k-1} = \frac{a(1 - r^k)}{1 - r}$$

we prove

$$S_{k+1} = a + ar + ar^2 + \cdots + ar^k = \frac{a(1 - r^{k+1})}{1 - r}$$

Proof of Part II.   We are given that

$$S_k = \frac{a(1 - r^k)}{1 - r}$$

Adding the $(k + 1)$th term of the progression to both members of the above equation we have

$$S_{k+1} = S_k + ar^k = \frac{a(1 - r^k)}{1 - r} + ar^k$$

$$= \frac{a - ar^k + ar^k - ar^{k+1}}{1 - r}$$

$$= \frac{a - ar^{k+1}}{1 - r} = \frac{a(1 - r^{k+1})}{1 - r}$$

This establishes the lemma: if the theorem is true for $n = k$, it is true for $n = k + 1$.

Part III.   In I we have observed that the theorem is true for $n = 1, 2,$ and 3.   Employing II it is true for $n = 4$; again by II it is true for $n = 5$; and so on by continuing to employ II it is true for $n = n$.   Therefore,

$$S_n = \frac{a(1 - r^n)}{1 - r}$$

is true for all positive integral values of n.

Example 2. Prove by mathematical induction that $x - y$ is a factor of $x^n - y^n$ for all positive integral values of n.

Proof.

Part I. We know that $\dfrac{x - y}{x - y} = 1$, $\dfrac{x^2 - y^2}{x - y} = x + y$, $\dfrac{x^3 - y^3}{x - y} = x^2 + xy + y^2$. Hence, $x - y$ is a factor of $x^n - y^n$ when $n = 1, 2,$ and 3.

Part II. We now prove that if the theorem is true for $n = k$, then it is true for $n = k + 1$. That is, if $x - y$ is a factor of $x^k - y^k$, then it is a factor of $x^{k+1} - y^{k+1}$. To show this we write

$$x^{k+1} - y^{k+1} = x^{k+1} - xy^k + xy^k - y^{k+1}$$
$$= x(x^k - y^k) + y^k(x - y)$$

Now $x - y$ is clearly a factor of $y^k(x - y)$. By hypothesis it is a factor of $x^k - y^k$. Hence it is a factor of both terms of the right-hand member. Therefore, if $(x - y)$ is a factor of $x^k - y^k$, it is a factor of $x^{k+1} - y^{k+1}$.

Part III. By I, $x - y$ is a factor of $x^n - y^n$ when $n = 1, 2,$ and 3. Therefore by II it is a factor of $x^n - y^n$ when $n = 4$; by II again when $n = 5$; and so on to any positive integral value $n = n$.

3. Notation for Sums. For the sake of brevity in writing the sums of series it is customary to use the Greek letter Σ (sigma) to designate "the sum of such terms as." Thus we write

$$u_1 + u_2 + u_3 + \cdots + u_n = \sum_1^n u_x$$

which is read "the sum of the numbers u_x, where x assumes all integral values from 1 to n inclusive." We call Σ the sign of summation. The numbers 1 and n are the lower and upper limits of the summation. If no limits are stated it is assumed they are 1 and n. The following illustrations will clarify the meaning of the symbol:

$$\sum_1^n x^2 = 1^2 + 2^2 + 3^2 + \cdots + n^2$$

$$\Sigma \frac{1}{x(x + 1)} = \frac{1}{1 \cdot 2} + \frac{1}{2 \cdot 3} + \frac{1}{3 \cdot 4} + \cdots + \frac{1}{n(n + 1)}$$

$$\sum_0^{n-1} 3^x = 1 + 3 + 3^2 + \cdots + 3^{n-1}$$

Example 3.   Prove by mathematical induction that

$$\Sigma \frac{1}{x(x+1)} = \frac{n}{n+1}$$

Proof.   Denoting the sum of the n terms by S_n, we are to prove that

$$S_n = \frac{1}{1\cdot2} + \frac{1}{2\cdot3} + \frac{1}{3\cdot4} + \cdots + \frac{1}{n(n+1)} = \frac{n}{n+1}$$

Part I.   We have

$$S_1 = \frac{1}{1\cdot2} = \frac{1}{1+1}$$

$$S_2 = \frac{1}{1\cdot2} + \frac{1}{2\cdot3} = \frac{2}{3} = \frac{2}{2+1}$$

$$S_3 = \frac{1}{1\cdot2} + \frac{1}{2\cdot3} + \frac{1}{3\cdot4} = \frac{3}{4} = \frac{3}{3+1}$$

and thus the theorem is true for $n = 1, 2,$ and 3.

Part II.   We now will prove that if $S_k = \dfrac{k}{k+1}$ then

$$S_{k+1} = \frac{k+1}{(k+1)+1}$$

We accomplish this by adding the $(k+1)$th term of the series, $\dfrac{1}{(k+1)(k+2)}$, to both members of $S_k = \dfrac{k}{k+1}.$ We have

$$S_{k+1} = S_k + \frac{1}{(k+1)(k+2)} = \frac{k}{k+1} + \frac{1}{(k+1)(k+2)}$$

$$= \frac{k+1}{k+2} = \frac{k+1}{(k+1)+1}$$

which proves the lemma: if $S_k = \dfrac{k}{k+1},$ then $S_{k+1} = \dfrac{k+1}{(k+1)+1}.$

Part III.   By I, $S_n = \dfrac{n}{n+1}$ is true when $n = 1, 2,$ and 3.   Hence by II it is true for $n = 4$; by II again it is true for $n = 5$; and so on for any positive integral value $n = n$.   Therefore.

$$S_n = \Sigma \frac{1}{x(x+1)} = \frac{n}{n+1}$$

Exercises

1. Prove: $\Sigma x^2 = \dfrac{n(n+1)(2n+1)}{6}$.

2. Prove: $\Sigma x^3 = \left[\dfrac{n(n+1)}{2}\right]^2 = [\Sigma x]^2$

3. Prove: $\Sigma \dfrac{1}{(2x-1)(2x+1)} = \dfrac{n}{2n+1}$.

4. Prove: $\Sigma n(n+1) = \dfrac{n(n+1)(n+2)}{3}$.

5. Derive the theorem: $\Sigma[U_x + V_x - W_x] = \Sigma U_x + \Sigma V_x - \Sigma W_x$.

6. Derive the theorem: $\Sigma c U_x = c \Sigma U_x$, c a constant.

7. Show that $\Sigma(2x-1) = n^2 + 1$ satisfies Part II of the proof by induction but not Part I.

8. Show that $\Sigma(2x-1) = n^2 + (n-1)(n-2)(n-3) \cdots (n-100)$ satisfies Part I of the proof by induction for $n = 1, 2, 3, \cdots, 100$, but not Part II.

9. Prove: $\dfrac{d^n(e^{ax})}{dx^n} = a^n e^{ax}$.

10. Prove: $\dfrac{d^n \sin ax}{dx^n} = a^n \sin\left(ax + \dfrac{n\pi}{2}\right)$.

11. Prove: $\dfrac{d^n \cos ax}{dx^n} = a^n \cos\left(ax + \dfrac{n\pi}{2}\right)$.

12. Prove: $\dfrac{d^{2n} \sin ax}{dx^{2n}} = (-1)^n a^{2n} \sin ax$.

13. Prove that $5^{2n} + 7$ is a multiple of 8.

Hint: $5^{2(k+1)} + 7 = 5^{2(k+1)} + 7(25) - 7(25) + 7$.

14. Prove: $\dfrac{d^n(\ln x)}{dx^n} = (-1)^{n+1} \cdot \dfrac{(n-1)!}{x^n}$.

15. Prove: $\dfrac{d^n(xe^x)}{dx^n} = (x+n)e^x$.

16. Prove by induction Leibnitz Theorem: $D^n uv = \displaystyle\sum_{i=0}^{n} \binom{n}{i} D^i u D^{n-i} v$

Appendix II

HYPERBOLIC FUNCTIONS

In the study of the infinitesimal calculus the student has doubtless encountered the Euler relations

$$e^{i\theta} = \cos\theta + i\sin\theta$$

$$e^{-i\theta} = \cos\theta - i\sin\theta$$

(where $i = \sqrt{-1}$), from which we derive the exponential values for $\sin\theta$ and $\cos\theta$, namely,

$$\sin\theta = \frac{e^{i\theta} - e^{-i\theta}}{2i}$$

$$\cos\theta = \frac{e^{i\theta} + e^{-i\theta}}{2}$$

The values of $\csc\theta$ and $\sec\theta$ are defined as the reciprocals of the above expressions defining $\sin\theta$ and $\cos\theta$. The formulas for $\tan\theta$ and $\cot\theta$ are defined as follows:

$$\tan\theta = \frac{\sin\theta}{\cos\theta} = \frac{1}{i}\left[\frac{e^{i\theta} - e^{-i\theta}}{e^{i\theta} + e^{-i\theta}}\right]$$

$$\cot\theta = \frac{\cos\theta}{\sin\theta} = i\left[\frac{e^{i\theta} + e^{-i\theta}}{e^{i\theta} - e^{-i\theta}}\right]$$

Somewhat similar functions, called hyperbolic functions, are frequently met in mathematics. Thus, the hyperbolic sine and the hyperbolic cosine are abbreviated and defined by the equations

$$\sinh u = \frac{e^u - e^{-u}}{2}$$

$$\cosh u = \frac{e^u + e^{-u}}{2}$$

136

These functions are so named because they have the same relation to the equilateral hyperbola $x^2 - y^2 = 1$ that the ordinary trigonometric functions, sometimes called circular functions, have to the circle $x^2 + y^2 = 1$.

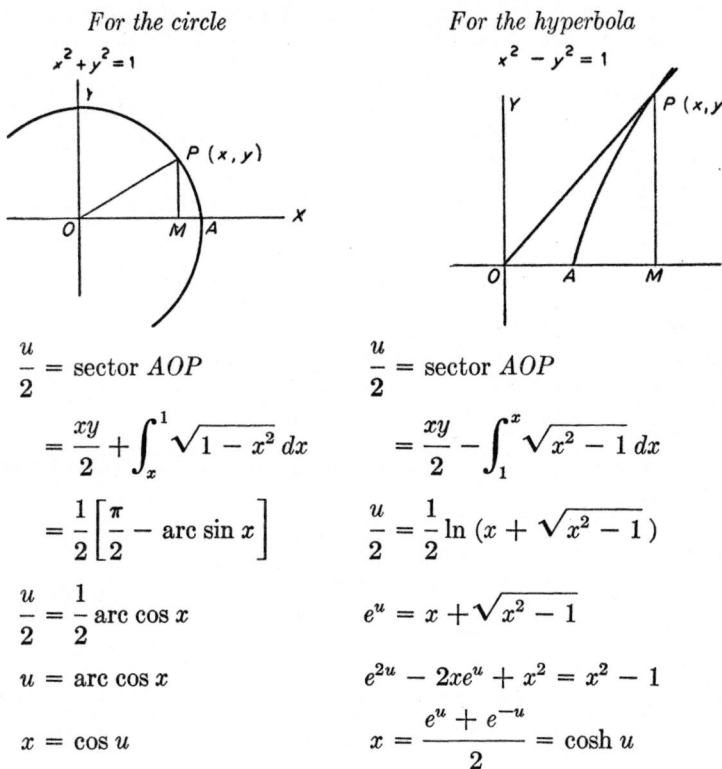

For the circle	*For the hyperbola*

$$\frac{u}{2} = \text{sector } AOP \qquad\qquad \frac{u}{2} = \text{sector } AOP$$

$$= \frac{xy}{2} + \int_x^1 \sqrt{1 - x^2}\, dx \qquad = \frac{xy}{2} - \int_1^x \sqrt{x^2 - 1}\, dx$$

$$= \frac{1}{2}\left[\frac{\pi}{2} - \text{arc sin } x\right] \qquad \frac{u}{2} = \frac{1}{2}\ln\left(x + \sqrt{x^2 - 1}\right)$$

$$\frac{u}{2} = \frac{1}{2}\text{arc cos } x \qquad\qquad e^u = x + \sqrt{x^2 - 1}$$

$$u = \text{arc cos } x \qquad\qquad e^{2u} - 2xe^u + x^2 = x^2 - 1$$

$$x = \cos u \qquad\qquad x = \frac{e^u + e^{-u}}{2} = \cosh u$$

In the circle in expressing x in terms of u we are led to the familiar $x = \cos u$. In the hyperbola we arrive at $x = (e^u + e^{-u})/2$. It is natural, analogously, to call this hyperbolic function the hyperbolic cosine, cosh u.

When we solve for y in terms of u we have

For the circle	*For the hyperbola*

$$y = \sqrt{1 - x^2} \qquad\qquad y = \sqrt{x^2 - 1}$$

$$= \sqrt{1 - \cos^2 u} \qquad\quad = \sqrt{\tfrac{1}{4}(e^u + e^{-u})^2 - 1}$$

$$= \sin u \qquad\qquad\quad = \frac{e^u - e^{-u}}{2}$$

$$= \sinh u$$

The other four hyperbolic functions are defined analogously to the corresponding circular functions:

$$\tanh u = \frac{\sinh u}{\cosh u} \qquad\qquad \operatorname{sech} u = \frac{1}{\cosh u}$$

$$\coth u = \frac{\cosh u}{\sinh u} \qquad\qquad \operatorname{csch} u = \frac{1}{\sinh u}$$

Exercises

1. $\sinh(-x) = -\sinh x$.

2. $\cosh(-x) = \cosh x$.

3. $\tanh(-x) = -\tanh x$.

4. $\cosh^2 x - \sinh^2 x = 1$.

5. $\operatorname{sech}^2 x = 1 - \tanh^2 x$.

6. $\operatorname{csch}^2 x = \coth^2 x - 1$.

7. $\cosh x + \sinh x = e^x$.

8. $\sin ix = i \sinh x$.

9. $\cos ix = \cosh x$.

10. $\tan ix = i \tanh x$.

11. $\cosh 2x = \cosh^2 x + \sinh^2 x$.

12. $\sinh 2x = 2 \sinh x \cosh x$.

13. $d \sinh u = \cosh u \, du$.

14. $d \cosh u = \sinh u \, du$.

15. $d \tanh u = \operatorname{sech}^2 u \, du$.

16. $\sinh \dfrac{x}{2} = \sqrt{\dfrac{\cosh x - 1}{2}}$.

17. $\cosh \dfrac{x}{2} = \sqrt{\dfrac{\cosh x + 1}{2}}$.

18. $\displaystyle\int \sinh u \, du = \cosh u + C$.

19. $\displaystyle\int \cosh u \, du = \sinh u + C$.

20. $\displaystyle\int \sinh^2 u \, du = \frac{1}{4} \sinh 2u - \frac{u}{2} + C$.

21. If $x = \sinh y$, show that $y = \sinh^{-1} x = \ln(x + \sqrt{x^2 + 1})$.

22. Draw graphs of the hyperbolic functions: $y = \sinh x$, $y = \cosh x$, $y = \tanh x$.

23. Derive:

(1) $\sin(x \pm iy) = \sin x \cosh y \pm i \cos x \sinh y$

(2) $\cos(x \pm iy) = \cos x \cosh y \mp i \sin x \sinh y$

24. Derive:

(1) $\sinh(x \pm iy) = \sinh x \cos y \pm i \cosh x \sin y$

(2) $\cosh(x \pm iy) = \cosh x \cos y \pm i \sinh x \sin y$

25. A function $f(x)$ is a periodic function of period k if $f(x + k) = f(x)$.

Establish the periodicity of the following hyperbolic functions. The corresponding relations for the circular functions are included for comparison.

$$\sinh(x + i2\pi) = \sinh x \qquad\qquad \sin(x + 2\pi) = \sin x$$
$$\cosh(x + i2\pi) = \cosh x \qquad\qquad \cos(x + 2\pi) = \cos x$$
$$\tanh(x + i\pi) = \tanh x \qquad\qquad \tan(x + \pi) = \tan x$$
$$\coth(x + i\pi) = \coth x \qquad\qquad \cot(x + \pi) = \cot x$$
$$\operatorname{csch}(x + i2\pi) = \operatorname{csch} x \qquad\qquad \csc(x + 2\pi) = \csc x$$
$$\operatorname{sech}(x + i2\pi) = \operatorname{sech} x \qquad\qquad \sec(x + 2\pi) = \sec x$$

26. Derive:

$$\sinh (x \pm y) = \sinh x \cosh y \pm \cosh x \sinh y$$
$$\cosh (x \pm y) = \cosh x \cosh y \pm \sinh x \sinh y$$

27. Derive:

$$\sinh (x + y) + \sinh (x - y) = 2 \sinh x \cosh y$$
$$\sinh (x + y) - \sinh (x - y) = 2 \cosh x \sinh y$$
$$\cosh (x + y) + \cosh (x - y) = 2 \cosh x \cosh y$$
$$\cosh (x + y) - \cosh (x - y) = 2 \sinh x \sinh y$$

28. Prove by mathematical induction that

$$(\cosh x + \sinh x)^n = \cosh nx + \sinh nx$$

INDEX